Mathematics

for Electrical and Telecommunications Technicians

VOLUME 2

Mathematics
for Electrical and
Telecommunications Technicians

VOLUME 2

J. L. Smithson

McGraw-Hill Book Company (UK) Limited

London · New York · St Louis · San Francisco · Auckland · Beirut
Bogotá · Düsseldorf · Johannesburg · Lisbon · Lucerne · Madrid
Mexico · Montreal · New Delhi · Panama · Paris · San Juan
São Paulo · Singapore · Sydney · Tokyo · Toronto

Published by
McGRAW-HILL Book Company (UK) Limited
MAIDENHEAD · BERKSHIRE · ENGLAND

07 094242 0

91011 pp 81079
Reproduced and printed by photolithography and bound in
Great Britain at The Pitman Press, Bath

To
Geoffrey and Lesley

Preface

One of the many essential qualities of a good teacher is to know his students and to get close to them in speech and thought. If they do not understand his language of communication, no progress will be made until he understands theirs. Once this happy state is achieved, students will feel that they are moving forward *with* their teacher and not simply struggling to follow him.

It is in this spirit that this book was written—with the difficulties of the student in mind. If the expression of a rule or formula has been repeated at several points in the book, this is good class-teaching technique; diagrams have received the same treatment. It is not good practice to refer to a diagram several pages previously; a new principle deserves its own diagram if one is required.

The scope of the work covers the requirements of the syllabuses in mathematics for the Electrical Engineering Technician courses of several examining boards and the Telecommunication Technicians' courses of the C.G.L.I., the latter being a 4-year course. The plan of this book takes into account the recently revised syllabuses of the City and Guilds of London Institute in respect of their Technician courses. I record with thanks, their co-operation in allowing me to use an advance copy of their publication. Students in the Mechanical Engineering Technician course, General Engineering, and O.N.C. courses will find the theory and many of the exercises in the book equally suitable for their syllabuses.

I have taught mathematics for thirty years in Technical and Grammar Schools and in Colleges of Further Education and this experience enables me to understand the academic background of the students for whom these books have been prepared. There are many worthy students in these courses who may have neglected their studies at school and who now realize the need for a mathematical understanding of their chosen vocation. With this in mind, the material has been developed from the very modest level of fractions and decimals in order to give every student the opportunity of a fresh start. The text is presented in detail and each step of calculations included; assumption of previous knowledge of a topic has been kept to an absolute minimum.

I have considered it useful to present the study of algebra as a topic which will be new to many students. In Vol. 1 a very close parallel is drawn between the numerical values of arithmetic and the letters, symbols and signs of algebra. Much importance is attached to the consideration of the processes which link together the various terms, factors, and expressions in algebra—a necessary analysis in the important subject of transposition of formulae.

Similar treatment of other subjects such as indices, logarithms, functions, trigonometry, and calculus, should enable students to learn successfully from these three volumes. The numerous exercises to be worked, have been carefully chosen so that students can practise new principles on simple questions, thereby acquiring a feeling of confidence before approaching the more difficult problems.

The ever-present quadratic equation has received adequate treatment in Vol. 2 over 10 pages. At all points, I have endeavoured to show the links connecting previous study with new work, as the sine function of simple trigonometry leads to period, frequency, and angular velocity; as the sine and cosine rules and Pythagoras' theorem assist the compounding of vectors; the progression of accuracy from the mid-ordinate rule to Simpson's rule and integration for areas applies to the computation of average and r.m.s. values. The development and use of the constant 'e' deserves its early position and full discussion as a sequel to a general discussion of 'Growth' in chapter 1 of Vol. 3. The same volume introduces the calculus on a basis of understanding and application rather than rigorous mathematical proof, which belongs to a later period of a student's development. Chapter 10 shows the complex number as another language of communication in the expression of data in vectorial problems.

Acknowledgement is due to the examination boards listed below for permission to use questions from their examination papers; the accuracy of the answers to these questions is my responsibility.

City and Guilds of London Institute   C.G.L.I.
East Midland Educational Union   E.M.E.U.
Northern Counties Technical Examinations Council N.C.T.E.C.

Union of Lancashire and Cheshire Institutes   U.L.C.I.
Yorkshire Council for Further Education   Y.C.

I am indebted to British Thornton Ltd., Manchester, for permission to use material from their instructional handbook on the Slide Rule. The section on Desk Calculators was written by Mr. L. R. Anderson, the Educational Adviser of Addo Ltd.; I am grateful for his contribution. I have received much encouragement from colleagues in the Department of Electrical Engineering at West Wythenshawe College of Further Education and I am thankful for their advice.

I owe an immeasurable debt of gratitude to my colleague of many years, J. F. G. Bigland, B.Sc. of Ilkley, for his patience and diligence in reading and revising the manuscript and checking every calculation in the three volumes.

J. L. Smithson

Notes

(a) At a late stage in the preparation of these volumes, it was decided that all units should conform to the rationalized metric system, known as SI. This has involved several hundreds of alterations in text and exercises, and while all necessary re-calculations have been checked, it is possible that a few errors have escaped notice.

Acknowledgement
I am particularly grateful to be able to use extracts (see pp. 97–103) from PD 5686 April 1967, *The Use of SI Units*, which are reproduced by permission of the British Standards Institution, 2, Park Street, London W.1, from whom copies of the complete publication may be obtained. This edition is being revised, but the main substance of Appendices A, B, and C will remain unaltered.

(b) Volume 1 covers the work in mathematics for the TI year of the Electrical, Telecommunications, and Electrical Installations Technicians courses (C and G 270 and 280).
Volume 2 covers E.T.2, Mathematics A of the Telecommunications Technicians course and 2nd year of the Electrical Technicians course (C and G 270 and 280).
Volume 3 covers the mathematics contained in the syllabuses for T3 Electrical Technicians courses (C and G 271 and 281).

Contents

1. Arithmetic and mensuration

1.1 Logarithms of numbers less than 1

In chapter 4 of Vol. 1, the development of the logarithms of numbers was seen to be associated with the study of indices; the definition of a logarithm refers to this connection.

'The logarithm of a number is the power to which the base is raised to equal the number.' The base for common logarithms is 10. Thus,

$$\log_{10} N = x, \qquad \therefore \ N = 10^x$$

The work of chapter 4, Vol. 1 can now be extended to numbers less than 1, for which it is useful to recall the results of §4.11 of Vol. 1, which deals with negative indices:

$$\frac{1}{a^m} = a^{-m}$$

We have obtained the logarithms of numbers by writing them as powers of 10. Let us apply this method to the number 0·03 and compare our result with the similar process applied to the number 3 as in chapter 4 of Vol. 1:

$$0 \cdot 03 = \frac{3}{100} = \frac{3}{10^2} = 3 \times 10^{-2}$$

Since the logarithm of 3 is 0·4771, then $3 = 10^{0 \cdot 4771}$. Hence

$$0 \cdot 03 = 3 \times 10^{-2} = 10^{0 \cdot 4771} \times 10^{-2}$$

$$= 10^{-2 + 0 \cdot 4771} \tag{1.1}$$

The addition of these powers, having regard to their signs, would lead to $10^{-1 \cdot 5229}$; this term does not then show any apparent connection with the digit 3 for which we have written $10^{0 \cdot 4771}$. Since the significant difference between 0·03 and 3 is a negative power of 10, this difference is preserved by writing (1.1) as $10^{\bar{2} \cdot 4771}$ (we say 'bar 2 point 4771'); this method retains the same decimal portion of the logarithm as for 3. It is important to remember that the integral part of the power, i.e., the characteristic, is negative, and the decimal part, i.e., the mantissa, is positive.

Hence $\log_{10} 0 \cdot 03 \;\; = \bar{2} \cdot 4771$

and $\log_{10} 0 \cdot 3 \;\;\; = \bar{1} \cdot 4771$

and $\log_{10} 0 \cdot 003 = \bar{3} \cdot 4771$

In using the logarithms of numbers which are less than 1, the first step is to write down the characteristic; this will be negative and numerically equal to the power of 10 required to write the given number in standard form.

Example 1.1.

Number	Number in standard form	Characteristic of logarithm
0·5137	$5 \cdot 137 \times 10^{-1}$	$\bar{1}$
0·0804	$8 \cdot 04 \;\; \times 10^{-2}$	$\bar{2}$
0·00076	$7 \cdot 6 \;\;\; \times 10^{-4}$	$\bar{4}$
0·001118	$1 \cdot 118 \times 10^{-3}$	$\bar{3}$

The decimal portion of the logarithm is then read from the tables as explained in chapter 4, Vol. 1, using only the significant figures of the number; for 0·0804, read line 80, column 4 in the tables.

1.2   Use of logarithms with negative characteristics

Example 1.2. Multiply 0·7615 by 32·94.

The practice of estimating the answer as a check on the position of the decimal point should be continued. Hence

$$0 \cdot 7615 \times 32 \cdot 94 = 0 \cdot 7 \times 30 \text{ approx.}$$

$$= 21 \text{ approx.}$$

No.	log
0·7615	$\bar{1}$·8817
32·94	1·5177
25·08	1·3994

Answer: 25·08.

It should be remembered that in the addition of the logarithms, any 'carrying figure' from the decimal part is positive.

Thus $\qquad\qquad\qquad\qquad\bar{1}$·8

add $\qquad\qquad\qquad$ 1·5

$\qquad\qquad\qquad\qquad\qquad\overline{1\cdot3}$

Example 1.3. Multiply 0·0219 by 0·4508.
Estimate: $0·02 \times 0·5 = 0·01$ approx.

No.	log
0·0219	$\bar{2}$·3404
0·4508	$\bar{1}$·6540
0·009872	$\bar{3}$·9944

Answer: 0·009872.

Example 1.4. Divide 5·762 by 0·3701.
Estimate: $6 \div 0·4 = 15$ approx.

No.	log
5·762	0·7606
0·3701	$\bar{1}$·5683
15·57	1·1923

Answer: 15·57.

Example 1.5. Divide 0·2124 by 3·142.
Estimate: $0·2 \div 3 = 0·07$ approx.

No.	log
0·2124	$\bar{1}$·3271
3·142	0·4972
0·06759	$\bar{2}$·8299

Answer: 0·06759.

Example 1.6. Divide 0·7813 by 0·0049.
Estimate: $1 \div 0·005 = 200$ approx.

No.	log
0·7813	$\bar{1}$·8929
0·0049	$\bar{3}$·6902
159·5	2·2027

Answer: 159·5.

Difficulties arising from the subtraction of the negative characteristics, as in Example 1.6, can be overcome if the student visualizes $\bar{1}$ subtract $\bar{3}$ as

$$-1 - (-3) = -1 + 3$$
$$= 2$$

A second check on correct subtraction can be applied if the last two lines of logarithms are added; this should equal the first line.

1.3   Evaluation of powers and roots of numbers, using logarithms

(a) Since $a^2 = a \times a$

then $\log(a^2) = \log(a \times a)$
$$= \log a + \log a$$
$$= 2 \log a$$

(b) Since $a^{1/2} \times a^{1/2} = a$

then $\log (a^{1/2} \times a^{1/2}) = \log a$
$$\therefore \log (a^{1/2}) + \log (a^{1/2}) = \log a$$
$$\therefore 2 \log (a^{1/2}) = \log a$$
$$\therefore \log (a^{1/2}) = \tfrac{1}{2} \log a$$

(c) Since $a^{-2} = \dfrac{1}{a^2}$

then $\log (a^{-2}) = \log \left(\dfrac{1}{a^2} \right)$

$$= \log 1 - \log (a^2)$$
$$= 0 - \log (a^2)$$
$$= -2 \log a$$

In general, $\log (a^n) = n \log a$, for all values of n, integral, fractional, positive, or negative.

Example 1.7. Evaluate $\sqrt{28 \cdot 49}$ by use of logarithms.

$$\sqrt{28 \cdot 49} = 28 \cdot 49^{1/2}$$

$$\therefore \log \sqrt{28 \cdot 49} = \tfrac{1}{2} \log 28 \cdot 49$$

No.	log
28·49	1·4547
$\sqrt{28\cdot49}$	1·4547
	2
	0·7274

$$\therefore \sqrt{28\cdot49} = \text{antilog } 0\cdot7274$$
$$= 5\cdot338$$

Example 1.8. Evaluate $(0\cdot9814)^3$ by use of logarithms.

$$\log (0\cdot9814)^3 = 3 \log 0\cdot9814$$

No.	log
0·9814	$\bar{1}\cdot9919$
	3
	$\bar{1}\cdot9757$

$$\therefore (0\cdot9814)^3 = \text{antilog } \bar{1}\cdot9757$$
$$= 0\cdot9456$$

Example 1.9. Evaluate $\sqrt{(4\cdot72)^3}$ by use of logarithms.

$$\sqrt{(4\cdot72)^3} = (4\cdot72)^{3/2}$$

$$\therefore \log \sqrt{(4\cdot72)^3} = \frac{3}{2} \log 4\cdot72 = \frac{3 \log 4\cdot72}{2}$$

No.	log
4·72	0·6739
	3
$(4\cdot72)^3$	2·0217
$(4\cdot72)^{3/2}$	1·0109

$$\therefore \sqrt{(4\cdot72)^3} = \text{antilog } 1\cdot0109$$
$$= 10\cdot25$$

Example 1.10. Evaluate $\sqrt[3]{0\cdot7165}$ by use of logarithms.

$$\sqrt[3]{0\cdot7165} = (0\cdot7165)^{1/3}$$

$$\therefore \log \sqrt[3]{0\cdot7165} = \tfrac{1}{3} \log (0\cdot7165)$$

$$= \tfrac{1}{3}(\bar{1}\cdot8552)$$

$\bar{1}\cdot8552$ is partly negative (-1), and partly positive $(0\cdot8552)$. The division of this logarithm by 3 would involve a 'carrying figure' of -1 into a positive part of the logarithm; this is clearly impractical. $\bar{1}\cdot8552$ is $-1 + 0\cdot8552$; its value will not be altered if we add $(-2 + 2)$.

Hence
$$\bar{1}\cdot8552 = -1 + 0\cdot8552$$
$$\text{add} \quad -2 + 2$$
$$= -3 + 2\cdot8552$$
$$= \quad \bar{3} + 2\cdot8552$$
$$\therefore \ \bar{1}\cdot8552 \div 3 = \frac{\bar{3} + 2\cdot8552}{3}$$
$$= \bar{1} + 0\cdot9517$$
$$= \bar{1}\cdot9517$$
$$\therefore \ \log \sqrt[3]{0\cdot7165} = \bar{1}\cdot9517$$
$$\therefore \ \sqrt[3]{0\cdot7165} = \text{antilog } \bar{1}\cdot9517$$
$$= 0\cdot8948$$

Similarly
$$\bar{1}\cdot2705 \div 2 = \frac{\bar{2} + 1\cdot2706}{2} = \bar{1}\cdot6353$$

and
$$\bar{3}\cdot4802 \div 2 = \frac{\bar{4} + 1\cdot4802}{2} = \bar{2}\cdot7401$$

Such adjustments are necessary only when we are dividing a logarithm which has a negative characteristic.

Example 1.11. Evaluate $2\cdot5^{1\cdot35}$.

It is now advisable to make the following statement.

Let $A = 2\cdot5^{1\cdot35}$, therefore
$$\log A = \log 2\cdot5^{1\cdot35}$$
$$= 1\cdot35 \times \log 2\cdot5$$
$$= 1\cdot35 \times 0\cdot3979$$

The multiplication on the r.h.s. is now treated in the ordinary way of multiplying two numbers by means of logarithms.

No.	log
1·35	0·1303
0·3979	$\bar{1}$·5998
0·5371	$\bar{1}$·7301

$$\therefore \ \log A = 0\cdot5371$$

The value of writing down a l.h.s. to each step of the work is now more obvious; we have reached a result for log A and must therefore read the antilog of 0·5371 to find the value of A.

$$\therefore A = 3·444$$

Example 1.12. Evaluate $5^{-2·46}$.

Let $A = 5^{-2·46}$, therefore

$$\log A = \log (5^{-2·46})$$
$$= -2·46 \times \log 5$$
$$= -2·46 \times 0·6990$$

No.	log
2·46	0·3909
0·6990	$\bar{1}$·8445
1·720	0·2354

$$\therefore \log A = -1·720$$

At this stage, we are stating the value of a logarithm in completely negative form; this does not meet the conditions described in §1.1 and we adjust as follows:

$$\log A = -1·720$$
$$\therefore \log A = -2 + 0·280$$
$$= \bar{2}·280$$
$$\therefore A = 0·01905$$

Note. The term 0·280 is the numerical difference between 2 and 1·720.

Example 1.13. Evaluate $0·1931^{-1·4}$.

Let $A = 0·1931^{-1·4}$, therefore

$$\log A = \log (0·1931^{-1·4})$$
$$= -1·4 \times \log 0·1931$$
$$= -1·4 \times \bar{1}·2858$$
$$= -1·4(-1 + 0·2858)$$
$$= -1·4(-0·7142)$$
$$= 1·4 \times 0·7142$$

No.	log
1·4	0·1461
0·7142	$\bar{1}$·8538
0·9997	$\bar{1}$·9999

$$\therefore \log A = 0·9997$$
$$\therefore A = 9·993$$

Characteristic

There is an alternative method of finding the characteristic of the logarithm of a number, which has the advantage of the same rule applying to numbers greater and less than unity. Start with the units digit, counting zero for that position, and continue counting until the first significant figure is reached; the final count gives the characteristic of the logarithm. If the number is greater than unity, the direction of counting will have been towards the left and the characteristic will be positive; if the number is less than unity, the direction will have been towards the right and the characteristic will therefore have the opposite sign, i.e., negative.

Example 1.14. Write down the characteristics of the logarithms of (a) 253·7, (b) 0·085.

(a) units digit 3   count 0
    tens digit 5   count 1
    hundreds digit 2   count 2

$\qquad\qquad$ ∴ characteristic is 2

(b) units digit 0   count 0
    1st dec. place 0   count 1
    2nd dec. place 8   count 2

$\qquad\qquad$ ∴ characteristic is $\bar{2}$

EXERCISE 1.1

Evaluate questions 1 to 15 using logarithms; estimate the answer first.

1. $14·07 \times 0·7432$
2. $5·916 \times \times 0·1652$
3. $0·2481 \times 0·3910$
4. $0·0517 \times 0·8145$
5. $0·00028 \times 32·2$
6. $25·4 \div 0·45$
7. $0·8536 \div 2·97$
8. $0·4629 \div 0·0038$
9. $\dfrac{0·7536 \times 0·059}{0·00672}$
10. $\dfrac{1000}{1·76 \times 0·028}$
11. $27·08^{2·06}$
12. $16·54^{0·82}$
13. $0·9723^{0·48}$
14. $0·057^{-0·26}$
15. $\dfrac{1}{42·7^{1·64}}$

16. The capacitance of a cable is given by $\dfrac{0·0388K}{\log_{10}(D/d)}$ microfarads/km, where D and d are the outer and inner diameters respectively and K is

a constant for the dielectric. Evaluate when $D = 0.5$, $d = 0.063$, and $K = 3.9$.

Y.C.

17. Use logarithms to evaluate,

$$2\pi \times \sqrt[3]{\left\{ \left[\frac{(3 \times 21.5) - (7.5)^2}{2\pi} \right]^2 \right\}}$$

Y.C.

18. Use logarithms to evaluate,

$$H = \frac{M}{(d^2 + l^2)^{3/2}}$$

when $M = 333$, $d = 15.5$, and $l = 5.2$.

Y.C.

19. (a) Evaluate $(1145^{1/2} \times 16.45^{-2})^{1/3}$
    (b) If $P = kB^n f$, calculate by logarithms the value of P when $k = 0.04$, $B = 1.5$, $n = 1.6$, and $f = 50$. Express your answer to three significant figures.

U.L.C.I.

20. (a) Evaluate $\dfrac{1}{2\pi\sqrt{(2.250 \times 10^{-11} \times 4.504 \times 10^{-3})}}$

    (b) Evaluate $\dfrac{17.36^{0.5} \times 4.07^{-2}}{\sqrt[5]{\{(0.54)^3\}}}$

U.L.C.I.

21. Evaluate $\sqrt{\left\{ \dfrac{3.709^3 \times 0.0081^{1/4}}{0.1075 + 0.25^2} \right\}}$

U.L.C.I. (part Qn.)

22. The attenuation (α) of a telephone cable expressed in decibels (dB) is given by,

$$\alpha = 10 \log_{10} \left[\frac{\text{Power sent}}{\text{Power received}} \right]$$

If a length of cable has an attenuation of 27dB, what power must be transmitted at the sending end in order that 0·1 mW may be measured at the receiver?

1.4 Theory of logarithms

In numerical calculations using logarithms, we refer to 'common logarithms' having a base 10. In more general terms, using any base b, we can state the definition in the form,

$$\log_b N = y$$
$$\therefore N = b^y$$

Example 1.15. Write down the value of $\log_4 64$.

Let $\log_4 64 = y$, then

$$64 = 4^y$$
$$\therefore 4^3 = 4^y$$
$$\therefore 3 = y$$
$$\therefore \log_4 64 = 3$$

Example 1.16. Evaluate $\log_3 (\frac{1}{27})$.

Let $\log_3 (\frac{1}{27}) = y$, then

$$\frac{1}{27} = 3^y$$
$$\therefore \frac{1}{3^3} = 3^y$$
$$\therefore 3^{-3} = 3^y$$
$$\therefore -3 = y$$
$$\therefore \log_3 (\frac{1}{27}) = -3$$

Example 1.17. If $\log_b 32 = 5$, find the value of b.

$$\log_b 32 = 5$$
$$\therefore 32 = b^5$$
$$\therefore 2^5 = b^5$$
$$\therefore 2 = b$$

Example 1.18. Determine the relation between $\log_a b$ and $\log_b a$.

Let $\log_a b = z$ and let $\log_b a = y$, then $b = a^z$ and $a = b^y$.
In $b = a^z$, raise each side to the power $1/z$:

$$b^{1/z} = (a^z)^{1/z} = a^{z \times 1/z}$$
$$\therefore b^{1/z} = a$$

Using this with the second equation, $a = b^y$:

$$b^{1/z} = b^y$$
$$\therefore \frac{1}{z} = y$$
$$\therefore \frac{1}{\log_a b} = \log_b a$$

Example 1.19. If $3^{2\cdot2} = 11\cdot21$, write down $\log_3 11\cdot21$.

Since the power of 3 required to equal $11\cdot21$ is $2\cdot2$, then this power is the logarithm of $11\cdot21$ to base 3.

$$\therefore \log_3 11\cdot21 = 2\cdot2$$

Change of base of logarithms

Suppose that the logarithm of a number N is given to a base b, and it is required to change this base to a.

Let $\log_b N = y$, then

$$N = b^y$$

Let $\log_a N = z$, then

$$N = a^z$$
$$\therefore b^y = a^z$$

Taking logarithms of both sides to base a,

$$y \times \log_a b = z \times \log_a a$$

but $\log_a a = 1$, since $a^1 = a$ (see §1.4),

$$\therefore y \times \log_a b = z$$
$$\therefore \log_b N \times \log_a b = \log_a N$$

A useful method of memorizing this relation is shown below; it must be emphasized that this is purely a memory aid and is not connected with the mathematical theory of logarithms.

Regard $\log_b N$ as N/b, $\log_a b$ as b/a, and $\log_a N$ as N/a. Hence

$$\frac{N}{b} \times \frac{b}{a} = \frac{N}{a}$$

Example 1.20. Write $\log_2 6$ as an equivalent logarithm to base 3.

$$\log_3 6 = \log_2 6 \times \log_3 2$$

1.5 Properties of logarithms

(a) $\log (pq) = \log p + \log q$

(b) $\log \left(\dfrac{p}{q}\right) = \log p - \log q$

(c) $\log (p^n) = n \times \log p$

(d) $\log \sqrt[n]{p} = \log (p^{1/n}) = \dfrac{1}{n} \times \log p$

Example 1.21. Given $\log 2 = 0.3010$ and $\log 3 = 0.4771$, write down the logarithms of the following numbers without the use of tables; it is assumed that all the logarithms refer to base 10.

$$\text{(a) } 20; \quad \text{(b) } 0.12; \quad \text{(c) } 3.6$$

(a)
$$\begin{aligned} \log 20 &= \log(2 \times 10) \\ &= \log 2 + \log 10 \\ &= 0.3010 + 1 \\ &= 1.3010 \end{aligned}$$

(b)
$$\begin{aligned} \log 0.12 &= \log\left(\frac{2^2 \times 3}{100}\right) \\ &= \log 2^2 + \log 3 - \log 100 \\ &= 2 \times \log 2 + \log 3 - \log 100 \\ &= 2 \times 0.3010 + 0.4771 - 2 \\ &= 0.6020 + 0.4771 - 2 \\ &= 1.0791 - 2 \\ &= 0.0791 - 1 \\ &= \bar{1}.0791 \end{aligned}$$

(c)
$$\begin{aligned} \log 3.6 &= \log\left(\frac{2^2 \times 3^2}{10}\right) \\ &= \log(2^2) + \log(3^2) - \log 10 \\ &= 2 \times \log 2 + 2 \times \log 3 - \log 10 \\ &= 2 \times 0.3010 + 2 \times 0.4771 - 1 \\ &= 0.6020 + 0.9542 - 1 \\ &= 0.5562 \end{aligned}$$

Example 1.22. Simplify (a) $\dfrac{\log 27}{\log 9}$, (b) $\dfrac{\log \frac{1}{16}}{\log \sqrt{2}}$.

(a)
$$\begin{aligned} \frac{\log 27}{\log 9} &= \frac{\log 3^3}{\log 3^2} \\ &= \frac{3 \times \log 3}{2 \times \log 3} \\ &= \frac{3}{2} \end{aligned}$$

(b)

$$\frac{\log \frac{1}{16}}{\log \sqrt{2}} = \frac{\log \left(\frac{1}{2^4}\right)}{\log (2^{1/2})}$$

$$= \frac{\log (2^{-4})}{\log (2^{1/2})}$$

$$= \frac{-4 \times \log 2}{\frac{1}{2} \times \log 2}$$

$$= -8$$

Example 1.23. Simplify the following and transform the logarithmic relation into an expression using powers; assume all the logarithms refer to base 10.

(a) $2 \times \log a + \log b = 4$
(b) $\log a - \frac{1}{2} \log b = 2$
(c) $a \times \log 3 + b \times \log 4 = -1$

(a)

$$2 \times \log a + \log b = 4$$
$$\therefore \ \log (a^2) + \log b = 4$$
$$\therefore \ \log_{10} (a^2 b) = 4$$
$$\therefore \ a^2 b = 10^4$$

(b)

$$\log a - \frac{1}{2} \log b = 2$$
$$\therefore \ \log a - \log (b^{1/2}) = 2$$
$$\therefore \ \log_{10} \left(\frac{a}{b^{1/2}}\right) = 2$$
$$\therefore \ \frac{a}{b^{1/2}} = 10^2 = 100$$
$$\therefore \ a = 100 \sqrt{b}$$

(c)

$$a \times \log 3 + b \times \log 4 = -1$$
$$\therefore \ \log 3^a + \log 4^b = -1$$
$$\therefore \ \log_{10} (3^a \times 4^b) = -1$$
$$\therefore \ 3^a \times 4^b = 10^{-1}$$
$$\therefore \ 3^a . 4^b = \frac{1}{10}$$

1.6   Exponential equations

Equations in which the unknown term occurs as a power are known as exponential equations. If it is recognized that the powers can be related to a common base, then the solution is reached by a comparison of powers. If no such base is evident, each term is referred to the common base of 10 by the use of logarithms.

Example 1.24. Solve the following equations:

$$\text{(a) } 9^{x+1} = 27^{x-1}, \quad \text{(b) } 5^a = 75$$

(a)
$$9^{x+1} = 27^{x-1}$$
$$\therefore \ (3^2)^{x+1} = (3^3)^{x-1}$$
$$\therefore \ 3^{2x+2} = 3^{3x-3}$$
$$\therefore \ 2x + 2 = 3x - 3$$
$$\therefore \ x = 5$$

(b)
$$5^a = 75$$

Taking logarithms of both sides,

$$\therefore \ \log (5^a) = \log 75$$
$$\therefore \ a \times \log 5 = \log 75$$
$$\therefore \ a = \frac{\log 75}{\log 5} = \frac{1 \cdot 8751}{0 \cdot 6990}$$

No.	log
1·875	0·2729
0·6990	$\bar{1}$·8445
2·681	0·4284

$$\therefore \ a = 2 \cdot 681$$

Example 1.25. Find the least integral value of n such that $(1 \cdot 02)^n$ exceeds $3 \cdot 2$.

Let $(1 \cdot 02)^n = 3 \cdot 2$, then

$$\log (1 \cdot 02)^n = \log 3 \cdot 2$$
$$\therefore \ n \times \log 1 \cdot 02 = \log 3 \cdot 2$$
$$\therefore \ n = \frac{\log 3 \cdot 2}{\log 1 \cdot 02}$$
$$= \frac{0 \cdot 5051}{0 \cdot 0086}$$

No.	log
0·5051	$\bar{1}$·7034
0·0086	$\bar{3}$·9345
58·73	1·7689

$$\therefore n = 58\text{·}73$$

Thus, for $(1\text{·}02)^n$ to exceed 3·2, n must have the value 59.

EXERCISE 1.2

Write down the values of the following logarithms without the use of tables

1. $\log_2 8$
2. $\log_5 125$
3. $\log_2 16$
4. $\log_6 \frac{1}{36}$
5. $\log_9 27$
6. $\log_{32} 64$
7. $\log_5 \frac{1}{25}$
8. $\log_{49} \sqrt{7}$
9. $\log_3 \frac{1}{81}$
10. $\log_6 216$

Insert the required factor to complete the following conversions.

11. $\log_4 6 = \log_8 6 \times \cdots$
12. $\log_7 5 = \log_{10} 5 \times \cdots$
13. $\log_2 0\text{·}8 = \log_3 0\text{·}8 \times \cdots$
14. $\log_b a = \log_c a \times \cdots$
15. $\log_e N = \log_{10} N \times \cdots$
16. Given that $\log 6 = 0\text{·}7782$ and $\log 2 = 0\text{·}3010$, find $\log 3$ without using tables.

N.C.T.E.C. (part Qn.)

17. If $\log_{10} 7 = x$ and $\log_{10} 2 = y$, express $\log_{10} 28$, $\log_{10} 24\text{·}5$, and $\log_{10} 1\text{·}75$ in terms of x and y.

E.M.E.U. (part Qn.)

18. If $(10^{0\text{·}3495})^2 = 5$, what is the logarithm of 5 to base 10?

E.M.E.U. (part Qn.)

19. Express as a formula without logarithms, $\log p = 2 - n \log v$.

U.E.I. (part Qn.)

20. If $\log 2 = 0\text{·}30103$ and $\log 3 = 0\text{·}47712$, find the values, without tables, of (a) $\log 6$, (b) $\log 12$, (c) $\log 27$, (d) $\log 5$.

U.E.I. (part Qn.)

21. Express $\frac{1}{2} \log P + 2 \log Q - 1$ as a single logarithm. (Assume that the logarithms are to base 10.)

Y.C. (part Qn.)

22. Without using tables, evaluate,

$$\frac{\log_{10} 16 - \log_{10} 2}{\log_{10} 4}$$

Y.C. (part Qn.)

23. Solve for x:

(a) $\log 3 + \log 4 - \log 6 = \log x$

(b) $4 \log 2 + \log 4 - \log 8 = x \log 2$

C.G.L.I. T.T. (part Qn.)

24. Find the value of n for which

$$5 \cdot 012^n = 10^{2n-1}$$

E.M.E.U. (part Qn.)

25. If $\log_{10} P = \log_{10} L + 2 \log_{10} D - \frac{1}{2} \log_{10} W + 2$, determine an expression for P in terms of L, D, and W.

C.G.L.I. E.T. (part Qn.)

26. If $\log_{10} a = 1 + \frac{3}{2} \log_{10} 4$, calculate the value of a without using tables.

C.G.L.I. T.T. (part Qn.)

27. Solve $4^x = 16^{x+1}$

28. Solve $3^x = 8^{x+1}$

29. The charge on a capacitor is falling and the voltage V at any time t sec is given by $V = V_0 e^{-kt}$, where V_0 is the original voltage and k is a constant. If $V_0 = 200$, $e = 2 \cdot 718$, and $k = 0 \cdot 0075$, find the value of V after $3 \cdot 5$ sec.

30. The formula $I = I_0 e^{-Rt/L}$ enables us to find the current I amperes which is flowing through a circuit containing inductance (L henrys) and resistance (R ohms) at a time t sec from the time at which the source of e.m.f. is removed. If the initial current is 500 mA, calculate the current which is flowing after 15 msec, if $L = 10$ henrys and $R = 400$ ohms. (Given e $= 2 \cdot 718$.)

C.G.L.I.

31. Given $P \cdot V^{1 \cdot 3} = C$, find the value of C when $P = 15$ and $V = 4 \cdot 32$. Find also the value of V when $P = 130$.

U.L.C.I. (part Qn.)

32. If T_1 and T_2 are the tensions in the two lengths of a belt which passes round a pulley, their ratio is given by

$$\frac{T_1}{T_2} = e^{\mu\theta}$$

where μ is the coefficient of friction and θ is the angle of contact of

the belt and pulley, measured in radians; e is a given constant
= 2·718.

Calculate T_2 if $T_1 = 150\,\text{N}, \mu = 0.3$, and $\theta = 5\pi/4$ radians.

1.7 Volumes and surface areas

(a) Cone

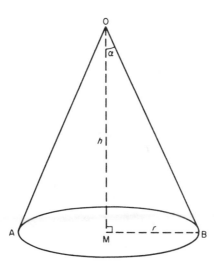

Fig. 1.1

$\angle\alpha$ = semi-vertical angle of cone.

Volume = $\frac{1}{3}\pi r^2 h$.

Curved surface area = $\pi r l$, where l is the slant length OA.

If we imagine a hollow cone of paper cut along AO and opened out, the
curved surface area becomes the area of a sector of a circle. The circumference of the base of the cone becomes the length of the arc ABA'.

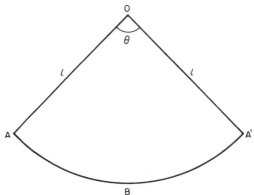

Fig. 1.2

In calculations involving sectors, it is useful to consider that a sector is a part of a circle; this fraction depends on the size of the angle θ.

$$\text{Length of arc ABA}' = \frac{\theta}{360°} \times 2\pi l$$

$$\text{Area of sector} = \frac{\theta}{360°} \times \pi l^2$$

Example 1.26. A sector of a circle of radius 10 cm has an angle of 120° at the centre. This sector is folded to make the curved surface area of a hollow cone. Calculate the radius of the base of the cone and its semi-vertical angle.

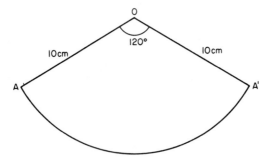

Fig. 1.3

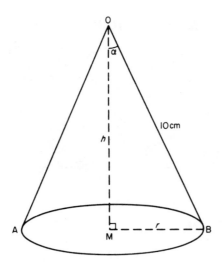

Fig. 1.4

Arc AA′ of sector is

$$\frac{120}{360} \times 2\pi10 = \frac{20\pi}{3} \text{ cm}$$

Therefore,

$$\text{Circumference of base of cone} = \frac{20\pi}{3} \text{ cm}$$

$$\therefore 2\pi r = \frac{20\pi}{3}$$

$$\therefore r = \frac{20\pi}{3} \times \frac{1}{2\pi} = \frac{10}{3}$$

$$= 3\dot{3} \text{ cm}$$

In $\triangle$OMB, $\qquad \sin \alpha = \dfrac{\text{MB}}{\text{OB}}$

$$= \frac{3\dot{3}}{10}$$

$$= 0\dot{3}$$

$$\therefore \alpha = 19° 28'$$

In problems concerning two or more figures derived from the circle, the term π should be carried into the final expression before evaluating; as in the above example, its numerical value is often not required.

Example 1.27. A sector of a circle of radius 12 cm has an area of 100π cm^2. Find the volume of the cone which could be made by folding this sector.

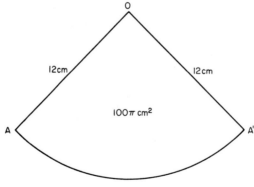

Fig. 1.5

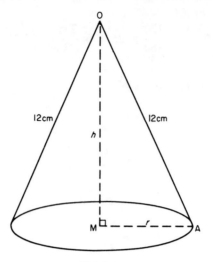

Fig. 1.6

$$\begin{pmatrix} \text{Curved surface area} \\ \text{of sector} \end{pmatrix} = \begin{pmatrix} \text{curved surface area} \\ \text{of cone} \end{pmatrix}$$

$$\therefore\ 100\pi = \pi r.12$$

$$\therefore\ \frac{100\pi}{12\pi} = r$$

$$\therefore\ r = \frac{25}{3}$$

In $\triangle OMA$,
$$12^2 = h^2 + \left(\frac{25}{3}\right)^2$$

$$\therefore\ 144 - \left(\frac{25}{3}\right)^2 = h^2$$

$$\therefore\ 144 - \frac{625}{9} = h^2$$

$$\therefore\ \frac{1296 - 625}{9} = h^2$$

$$\frac{671}{9} = h^2$$

$$\therefore \frac{\sqrt{671}}{3} = h$$

$$\therefore \frac{25 \cdot 9}{3} = h$$

$$\therefore h = 8 \cdot 6$$

$$\text{Volume of cone} = \frac{1}{3} \pi r^2 h$$

$$= \frac{1}{3} \cdot \frac{22}{7} \left(\frac{25}{3}\right)^2 8 \cdot 6$$

$$= 625 \text{ cm}^3 \quad \text{(S.R.)}^*$$

Frustum of a cone

If a plane section is made, parallel to the base of a cone, the portion above the section is a cone similar to the original cone, and the portion below the section is a frustum of a cone; this latter should always be considered as the difference between the original cone and the small cone cut off above the section. The geometry of similar triangles and similar solids is the key to calculations in this type of problem.

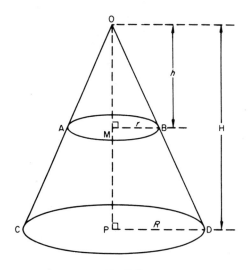

Fig. 1.7

* S.R. indicates the use of the Slide Rule.

From similar triangles, OMB and OPD,

$$\frac{r}{R} = \frac{h}{H}$$

$$\frac{\text{vol. of cone OAB}}{\text{vol. of cone OCD}} = \frac{r^3}{R^3} = \frac{h^3}{H^3}$$

Example 1.28. A solid cone of height 15 cm and base radius 9 cm is cut by a plane parallel to the base at a distance of 5 cm from the vertex. Calculate the volume and curved surface area of the portion above the section.

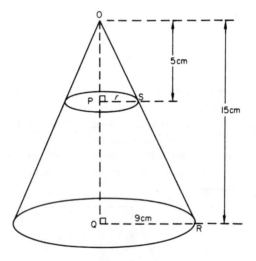

Fig. 1.8

From similar triangles OPS and OQR,

$$\frac{r}{9} = \frac{5}{15}, \quad \therefore r = \frac{5}{15} \times 9, \quad \therefore r = 3 \text{ cm}$$

$$\begin{aligned}
\text{Volume of small cone} &= \tfrac{1}{3}\pi r^2 h \\
&= \tfrac{1}{3}\pi 3^2 \times 5 \\
&= 47 \text{ cm}^3 \quad \text{(S.R.)}
\end{aligned}$$

In triangle OPS,

$$\begin{aligned}
OS^2 &= OP^2 + PS^2 \\
&= 5^2 + 3^2
\end{aligned}$$

$$\therefore \; OS = \sqrt{34}$$

Curved surface area $= \pi r l$

$$= \pi 3 \sqrt{34}$$
$$= 55 \cdot 0 \text{ cm}^2 \quad \text{(S.R.)}$$

Example 1.29. A solid cone has a height of 10 cm. At what distance from the vertex must a horizontal section be made to divide the cone into two equal volumes?

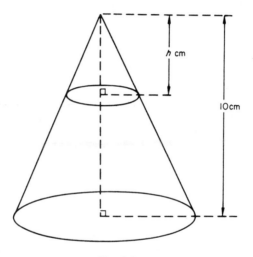

Fig. 1.9

Let the required distance be h cm from the vertex. By the geometry of similar solids,

$$\frac{h^3}{10^3} = \frac{\text{vol. of small cone}}{\text{vol. of original cone}} = \frac{1}{2}$$

$$\therefore \; \frac{h^3}{1000} = \frac{1}{2}$$

$$\therefore \; h^3 = 500$$

$$\therefore \; h = \sqrt[3]{500}$$

$$= 7 \cdot 94 \text{ cm} \quad \text{(S.R.)}$$

Example 1.30. A hopper is in the shape of a frustum of a cone. The radii of its ends are 3 m and 2 m and its vertical height is 6 m. Calculate the volume of the hopper.

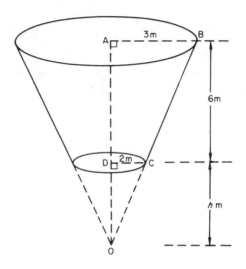

Fig. 1.10

From the similar triangles ODC, OAB,

$$\frac{h}{h + 6} = \frac{2}{3}$$

$$\therefore \ 3h = 2(h + 6)$$

$$\therefore \ h = 12 \text{ m}$$

Volume of frustum = volume of large cone
− volume of small cone

$$= \frac{1}{3}\pi 3^2 . 18 - \frac{1}{3}\pi 2^2 . 12$$

$$= \frac{1}{3}\pi (162 - 48)$$

$$= \frac{1}{3}\pi . 114$$

$$= 119 \text{ m}^3 \quad \text{(S.R.)}$$

(b) Pyramid

Consider a cube of edge 2*a* units in length.

The point O is the centre of the cube where all the diagonals intersect. Join O to the four vertices of the face ABCD. The figure O,ABCD is then a pyramid on a square base, with a vertical height a units; there will be six such pyramids forming the volume of the cube.

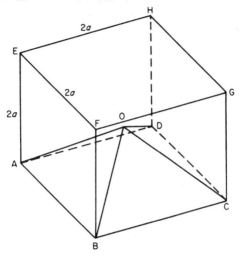

Fig. 1.11

Volume of pyramid O,ABCD $= \frac{1}{6} \times$ volume of cube

$$= \frac{1}{6} \times (2a)^3$$
$$= \frac{1}{6} \times 8a^3$$
$$= \frac{1}{6} \times 2a \times 4a^2$$
$$= \frac{1}{3} \times a \times 4a^2$$
$$= \frac{1}{3} \times \text{height} \times \text{area of base}$$

This then is the volume of a pyramid on any base, of which a cone is a special case.

(c) Sphere

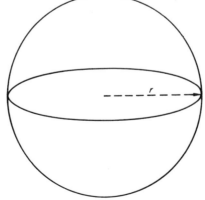

Fig. 1.12

Volume $= \frac{4}{3}\pi r^3$.   Surface area $= 4\pi r^2$

Spherical cap or segment

Any single plane section of a sphere produces a spherical cap or segment, a solid object bounded by two surfaces, a curved surface which is part of the original spherical surface and the plane surface of cross-section which is a circle.

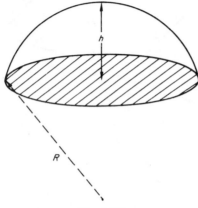

Fig. 1.13

The essential dimensions of a spherical cap are, the radius R of the sphere and h the height of the cap. From these dimensions, we can state,

$$\text{Volume of cap} = \frac{\pi h^2}{3}(3R - h)$$

$$\text{Curved surface area} = 2\pi R h$$

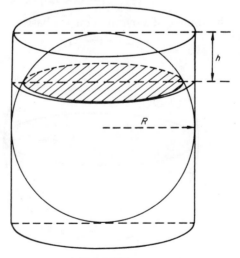

Fig. 1.14

The form of this last term reminds us of the curved surface area of a cylinder, with which there is a useful connection. (See Fig. 1.14.)

The curved surface area of any section of a sphere, formed either by a single plane or two parallel planes, is equal to the curved surface area, between the two planes, of the cylinder which encloses the whole sphere. The curved surface area of the spherical cap is equal to the curved surface area of that part of the enclosing cylinder of height h and radius R.

Spherical zone

This is the part of a sphere contained between two parallel plane sections of the sphere.

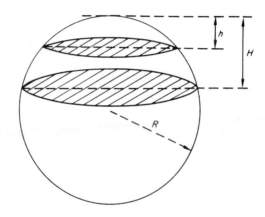

Fig. 1.15

The volume of the zone can be regarded as the difference between the volumes of two spherical caps of heights H and h.

$$\text{Volume of zone} = \frac{\pi H^2}{3}(3R - H) - \frac{\pi h^2}{3}(3R - h)$$

$$\text{Curved surface area} = 2\pi R(H - h)$$

Ratio of volumes of cone, sphere, and cylinder

$$\text{Volume of cone} = \tfrac{1}{3}\pi R^2.2R = \tfrac{2}{3}\pi R^3$$

$$\text{Volume of sphere} = \tfrac{4}{3}\pi R^3$$

$$\text{Volume of cylinder} = \pi R^2.2R = 2\pi R^3$$

$$\therefore \ V_{\text{cone}} : V_{\text{sphere}} : V_{\text{cylinder}} = 1:2:3$$

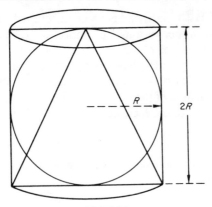

Fig. 1.16

Example 1.31. A solid cylinder of radius r and length l (greater than $r\sqrt{3}$) has a conical hole drilled in it at each end, coaxial with the cylinder. Each cone has a vertical angle of $60°$ and a base diameter r. Express in its neatest form the total surface area S of the resulting solid in terms of r and l.

C.G.L.I. T.T. (part Qn.)

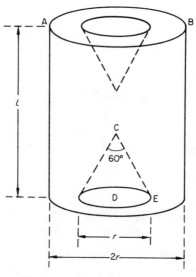

Fig. 1.17

$\triangle$CDE is a $90°$, $60°$, $30°$ triangle, hence

$$CE = 2DE = r$$

Vertical section
through AB

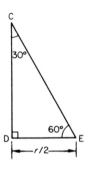

Fig. 1.18

The original total surface area of the cylinder has been increased by the curved surface areas of the two cones and diminished by the areas of the circular bases of the cones. Hence

$$S = (2\pi rl + 2\pi r^2) + 2\pi \frac{r}{2} r - 2\pi \left(\frac{r}{2}\right)^2$$

$$= 2\pi rl + 2\pi r^2 + \pi r^2 - \frac{\pi r^2}{2}$$

$$= 2\pi rl + \frac{5\pi r^2}{2}$$

$$= \frac{\pi}{2}(4rl + 5r^2)$$

Note. The condition stated in the question that l is greater than $r\sqrt{3}$ is to ensure that the length of the cylinder is sufficient to accommodate the vertical heights of the two cones, i.e.,

$$2 \times CD = 2 \times \frac{r\sqrt{3}}{2} = r\sqrt{3}$$

Example 1.32. A solid sphere is re-cast without loss of material to form a solid cylinder whose diameter equals its axial length. Calculate as a percentage, the resulting increase in surface area.

C.G.L.I. T.T. (part Qn.)

The direct connection between the dimensions of the sphere and cylinder is that their volumes are equal.

Let the radius of the cylinder be r and let the radius of the sphere be R. Therefore,

Length of cylinder is $2r$

$$\therefore \frac{4\pi R^3}{3} = \pi r^2 . 2r$$

$$\therefore \frac{4R^3}{3} = 2r^3$$

$$\therefore \frac{2R^3}{3} = r^3$$

$$R\sqrt[3]{\tfrac{2}{3}} = r$$

Surface area of sphere is $4\pi R^2$.
Total surface area of cylinder is

$$2\pi r^2 + 2\pi r . 2r = 6\pi r^2$$

In terms of R, the total surface area of the cylinder is

$$6\pi \left[R \sqrt[3]{\frac{2}{3}} \right]^2 = 6\pi R^2 \left[\left(\frac{2}{3}\right)^{1/3} \right]^2$$

$$= 6\pi R^2 \left(\frac{2}{3}\right)^{2/3}$$

$$\therefore \% \text{ change} = \frac{\text{actual change}}{\text{original value}} \times \frac{100}{1}$$

$$= \frac{6\pi R^2 \left(\dfrac{2}{3}\right)^{2/3} - 4\pi R^2}{4\pi R^2} \times \frac{100}{1}$$

$$= \frac{2\pi R^2 \left[3\left(\dfrac{2}{3}\right)^{2/3} - 2 \right]}{4\pi R^2} \times \frac{100}{1}$$

$$= \frac{\left[3 \times \dfrac{2^{2/3}}{3^{2/3}} - 2 \right]}{2} \times \frac{100}{1}$$

$$= [3^{1/3} \times 2^{2/3} - 2] \times 50$$

$$= [2 \cdot 290 - 2] \times 50$$

$$= 0 \cdot 290 \times 50$$

$$= 14 \cdot 5\%$$

No.	log
2	0·3010
∴ 2^2	0·6020
∴ $2^{2/3}$	0·2007
	0·1590 ◄┐
2·290	0·3597 ┊
3	0·4771 ┊
∴ $3^{1/3}$	0·1590 ┄┘

Example 1.33. A sphere of radius 2 cm rests inside an inverted hollow cone of radius 3 cm and height 5·5 cm. Calculate (a) the radius of the circle of contact, (b) the volume of the spherical cap remaining above the level of the base of the cone.

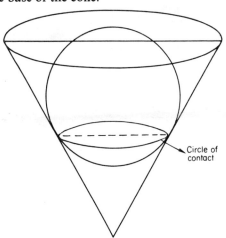

Fig. 1.19

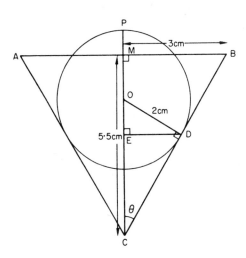

Fig. 1.20

(a) The radius of the circle of contact is ED.

In $\triangle CMB$,

$$\tan \theta = \frac{3}{5 \cdot 5} = 0 \cdot 545 \quad \text{(S.R.)}$$

$$\therefore \ \theta = 28° \ 36'$$

$$\therefore \ \angle EDC = 61° \ 24' \quad \text{since} \ \angle DEC = 90°$$

$$\therefore \ \angle EDO = 28° \ 36' \quad \text{since} \ \angle ODC = 90°$$

In $\triangle EDO$,

$$\frac{ED}{OD} = \cos \angle EDO = \cos 28° \ 36'$$

$$\therefore \ \frac{ED}{2} = 0 \cdot 8780$$

$$\therefore \ ED = 1 \cdot 7560 \ \text{cm}$$

(b) In $\triangle ODC$,

$$\frac{2}{CO} = \sin \theta$$

$$\therefore \ CO = \frac{2}{\sin \theta} = \frac{2}{\sin 28° \ 36'}$$

$$= 4 \cdot 18 \quad \text{(S.R.)}$$

$$CP = CO + OP$$

$$= 4 \cdot 18 + 2 = 6 \cdot 18$$

$$\therefore \ MP = 6 \cdot 18 - 5 \cdot 5 = 0 \cdot 68 \ \text{cm}$$

Volume of spherical cap is

$$\frac{\pi h^2}{3} (3R - h) = \frac{\pi (0 \cdot 68)^2}{3} (6 - 0 \cdot 68)$$

$$= 2 \cdot 58 \ \text{cm}^3 \quad \text{(S.R.)}$$

EXERCISE 1.3

1. Find (a) the volume and (b) the total surface area of a spherical cap of height 2·5 cm cut from a sphere of radius 4·5 cm.

2. If a spherical cap has a height equal to half the radius of the sphere from which it is cut, what fraction of the sphere is the cap (a) in volume, and (b) in curved surface area?

3. A sphere, radius 6 cm floats in water so that its maximum height above the water-level is 10·5 cm. Calculate the radius of the water-line.

4. When 100 spherical ball-bearings are immersed in liquid contained in a cylinder of radius 3 cm, the level of liquid rises by 1·5 cm. Calculate the radius of a ball-bearing.

5. A solid cylindrical bar of metal, radius 18 mm and length 0·5 m has a flat machined on to a depth of 7·5 mm. Calculate the amount of metal removed.

6. A tapered pin of length 150 mm, radii of ends 28 mm and 38 mm, is turned from a cylindrical rod of radius 38 mm. Calculate the volume of metal removed.

7. Sheet metal in the form of an annulus, of internal and external radii 100 mm and 250 mm respectively, is cut along two radii including an angle of 240° at the centre. This piece of metal is then bent to form a hollow frustum of a cone. Calculate the volume of this frustum correct to three significant figures.

8. A right circular cone has the same base radius r, as the radius of a sphere, and its volume is twice that of the sphere. Calculate the vertical height of the cone in terms of r.

U.E.I. (part Qn.)

9. A solid cylindrical roller is 10 cm long and its total surface area, including the ends, is 100π cm^2. Calculate its radius.

U.L.C.I. (part Qn.)

10. A copper tube has an outer circumference of 75 mm and a cross-sectional area of 195 mm^2. The density of copper is 9 g/ml and the tube is filled with an insulating material whose density is 3·7 g/ml.

Determine, (a) the outer diameter of the tube; (b) the inner diameter of the tube; (c) the mass per metre run of the tube and insulating material.

Y.C.

11. A factory is producing steel rods of hexagonal cross-section, 3 m long, the section having dimension of 200 mm across the flats. Calculate the weight of a rod, if the density of the steel is 7850 kg/m^3.

It is found that one rod weighs 0·25 kg less than the correctly formed rod. If this is due to a spherical cavity (bubble) formed inside the rod during manufacture, calculate the diameter of the cavity. (Take $\pi = \frac{22}{7}$)

Y.C.

12. A bar of steel, 4 cm diameter has a flat machined along its length
    so that in cross-section the angle subtended at the centre is 60°.
    Calculate the percentage of material removed in the process.

    U.E.I.

13. (a) Sketch (i) a sector of a circle, (ii) a segment of a circle.
    (b) A sector of a circle is cut from a sheet of metal and formed into
        a hollow right cone without a base. If the vertical height of the
        cone is 8·944 cm and the radius of the base 8 cm, and there is
        no overlapping of edges, calculate (i) the radius of the sector
        of the circle; (ii) the angle, in degrees, subtended at the centre
        of the sector; (iii) the area of the sector; (iv) the volume of the
        cone.

        U.L.C.I.

14. The total surface area of a cylindrical roller is 48π cm^2. If the roller
    is 10 cm long, calculate its radius.

    U.L.C.I. (part Qn.)

15. A tapered roller is 12 cm long. Its end radii are 1 and 3 cm. If the
    material of which it is made weighs 2·83 g/ml, calculate its weight.

    U.L.C.I.

16. A hot-water storage tank is a vertical cylinder surmounted by a
    hemisphere. If the diameter of the cylinder is 450 mm and the
    capacity of the tank is 225 l, calculate (a) the total height of the
    tank; (b) the area of lagging material required to enclose the tank,
    including the base.

    C.G.L.I. E.T.

17. A hollow container in the shape of a right circular cone of base
    radius 4·8 cm and vertical height 6·4 cm is made from sheet metal
    of negligible thickness. Calculate the total area of sheet metal used.
        The base of the cone is placed on a horizontal table and liquid
    poured in through a small hole at the top to a depth of 4·8 cm.
    Calculate the volume of air space remaining.

    C.G.L.I. T.T.

18. From a solid sphere of radius 10 cm, a zone is cut so that the radii
    of the plane faces are 8 cm and 6 cm. Calculate (a) the volume of
    the zone; (b) the curved surface area of the zone.

19. A solid is made up of a cone and a hemisphere. The base of the
    cone and the hemisphere are each 1 m in diameter. The height of
    the cone is 2·1 m, the total height of the solid being 2·6 m.
        Find the volume of the solid and also its weight if the density of
    the material is 400 kg/m^3.

    U.L.C.I.

20. A boss supported by triangular ribs is cast with a base plate, with dimensions as shown in Fig. 1.21. Calculate the weight of the component if the metal weighs 7 g/ml.

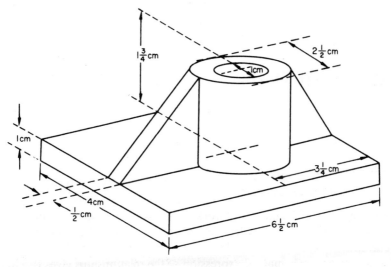

Fig. 1.21

2. Algebra

2.1 Simultaneous equations

Each part of a circuit or network, composed of different values of resistance, in series or parallel, and a source of e.m.f., will carry different currents. Kirchhoff's laws relate these currents and e.m.f.'s in such a way that the mathematical expression of the relationships gives rise to a series of simultaneous equations.

First law

The total current flowing towards a junction is equal to the total current flowing away from that junction, i.e., the algebraic sum of the currents at that point is zero.

Example 2.1.

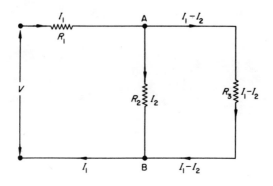

Fig. 2.1

At A, the current through R_1 is I_1, flowing towards A. Part of this current, I_2, will flow through R_2 away from A. Hence the remainder of the current, $I_1 - I_2$, will flow away from A through R_3.

Second law

In a closed circuit, the algebraic sum of the products of the current and resistance of each part of the circuit is equal to the resultant e.m.f. in the circuit.

Example 2.2.

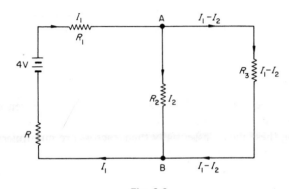

Fig. 2.2

The currents in each part of the circuit have been given the values I_1, I_2, and $I_1 - I_2$, by consideration of Kirchhoff's first law. Applying the second law to the circuit formed by the battery, R_1, R_2, and R, we obtain the equation,

$$4 = I_1 R_1 + I_2 R_2 + I_1 R \qquad (2.1)$$

For the circuit formed by the battery, R_1, R_3, and R, we obtain,

$$4 = I_1 R_1 + R_3(I_1 - I_2) + I_1 R \qquad (2.2)$$

In the given circuit, let $R = 2\Omega$, $R_1 = 10\Omega$, $R_2 = 6\Omega$, and $R_3 = 12\Omega$. Equations (2.1) and (2.2) now form a pair of simultaneous equations from which it is possible to calculate the values of I_1 and I_2.

From (2.1),

$$4 = 10I_1 + 6I_2 + 2I_1$$
$$\therefore \ 4 = 12I_1 + 6I_2 \qquad (2.3)$$

From (2.2),

$$4 = 10I_1 + 12(I_1 - I_2) + 2I_1$$
$$\therefore\ 4 = 24I_1 - 12I_2$$
$$\therefore\ 2 = 12I_1 - 6I_2 \qquad\qquad (2.4)$$

Adding equations (2.3) and (2.4),

$$4 = 12I_1 + 6I_2$$
$$2 = 12I_1 - 6I_2$$
$$\therefore\ 6 = 24I_1$$
$$\therefore\ I_1 = \tfrac{1}{4}\,\text{A}$$

Substituting this value of I_1 in equation (2.3) or (2.4), gives $I_2 = \tfrac{1}{6}$ A.

Hence the current through R and R_1 is $\tfrac{1}{4}$ A, through R_2, $\tfrac{1}{6}$ A, and through R_3 is $\tfrac{1}{12}$ A.

2.2   Factors

Factors have been described as the parts into which a given number can be divided. In reverse, the original number can be regained by multiplying these parts; essentially then, factors are multipliers. If we write $a(b + c)$, it is intended that each term within the bracket is multiplied by a; hence,

$$a(b + c) = ab + ac \qquad\qquad (2.5)$$

Since the expression on the right is the result of multiplying a and $(b + c)$, then these two quantities are factors of $ab + ac$.

If we write $(a + b)(c + d)$, each term in the first bracket multiplies each term in the second, thus producing four multiplications or four new terms.

$$(a + b)(c + d) = ac + ad + bc + bd \qquad\qquad (2.6)$$

It is much more useful to be able to take the r.h.s. of (2.5) and (2.6) and write them as factors as on the l.h.s. This process is known as factorization, for which there are several standard methods.

(1) Common factors; (2) Factors by grouping

These two methods are often required in the same expression. In (2.6), the expression $ac + ad + bc + bd$ contains an obvious repetition of factors, but the similarities do not extend throughout the whole expression.

a is a common factor of $ac + ad$

b is a common factor of $bc + bd$

Hence we write the expression in two groups,

$$(ac + ad) + (bc + bd)$$

from which we obtain

$$a(c + d) + b(c + d)$$

This now consists of two terms, namely $a(c + d)$ and $b(c + d)$, each containing a common factor $(c + d)$.
Hence

$$ac + ad + bc + bd = a(c + d) + b(c + d)$$
$$= (c + d)(a + b)$$

Example 2.3. Factorize $a^2 + ab + 5a + 5b$.

$$a^2 + ab + 5a + 5b = (a^2 + ab) + (5a + 5b) \quad \text{grouping terms,}$$
$$= a(a + b) + 5(a + b) \quad \text{common factors,}$$
$$= (a + b)(a + 5)$$

Example 2.4. Factorize $ad - af - pd + pf$.

$$ad - af - pd + pf = (ad - af) - (pd - pf) \quad \text{note change of sign}$$
$$= a(d - f) - p(d - f)$$
$$= (d - f)(a - p)$$

Example 2.5. Factorize $6ad + 2an - 12cd - 4cn$.

$$6ad + 2an - 12cd - 4cn$$
$$= (6ad + 2an) - (12cd + 4cn) \quad \text{note change of sign}$$
$$= 2a(3d + n) - 4c(3d + n)$$
$$= (3d + n)(2a - 4c)$$
$$= 2(3d + n)(a - 2c)$$

Example 2.6. Factorize $2 \sin^2 A - \sin A \cos A$.

$$2 \sin^2 A - \sin A \cos A = \sin A(2 \sin A - \cos A)$$

(3) Difference of two squares

The title of this type of factor describes exactly the construction of the expression to be factorized; two terms, each a perfect square, linked by subtraction. The standard example is $a^2 - b^2$ giving factors $(a + b)$ $(a - b)$.

Example 2.7. Factorize $4x^2 - 9y^2$.

$$4x^2 - 9y^2 = (2x + 3y)(2x - 3y)$$

Example 2.8. Factorize $\cos^2 A - \sin^2 A$.

$$\cos^2 A - \sin^2 A = (\cos A - \sin A)(\cos A + \sin A)$$

Example 2.9. Factorize $\pi R^2 - \pi r^2$.

$$\pi R^2 - \pi r^2 = \pi(R^2 - r^2)$$
$$= \pi(R - r)(R + r)$$

Example 2.10. Factorize $3x^2 - 12$.

$$3x^2 - 12 = 3(x^2 - 4)$$
$$= 3(x - 2)(x + 2)$$

(4) Quadratic factors

If two expressions, whose highest power is 1, are multiplied, the result is a quadratic function of the variable.

Example 2.11.

$$(x + 2)(x + 3) = x(x + 3) + 2(x + 3)$$
$$= x^2 + 3x + 2x + 6$$
$$= x^2 + 5x + 6$$

Therefore, the factors of $x^2 + 5x + 6$ are $(x + 2)(x + 3)$.

Example 2.12. Factorize $x^2 + 15x + 56$.

Recognizing the type of factors required, we choose factors of x^2 to fill the first terms in each bracket; $(x \quad)(x \quad)$.

x^2

The remaining choice is the pair of numerical factors of 56 to fill the second term in each bracket. Since this completes our factors, this pair must serve two purposes.

Their product gives 56:

$+56$

$$(x + 8)(x + 7)$$

and the two multiplications together give $15x$:

$$(x + 8)(x + 7)$$

$+8x$

$+7x$

If all these pairs of multiplications are carried out, it becomes a check on the correct choice of factors.

Only extensive practice will enable students to factorize quadratic expressions reasonably quickly. There are very few guides in this type of work.

(a) If the last term is positive, then each factor has the same sign.
Consider $x^2 \pm Nx + 8$; the possible factors are

$$(x + 8)(x + 1)$$
$$(x - 8)(x - 1)$$
$$(x + 4)(x + 2)$$
$$(x - 4)(x - 2)$$

In each case, the terms resulting in x, e.g.,

$$(x - 4)(x - 2) \quad \text{or} \quad (x + 8)(x + 1)$$

will have similar signs and therefore their sum must produce $\pm Nx$.

(b) If the last term of the quadratic expression is negative, then the factors will have opposite signs and the difference between the products resulting in terms in x will produce $\pm Nx$.

Example 2.13. Factorize $x^2 - x - 6$.

$$x^2 - x - 6 = (x - 3)(x + 2)$$

hence $-3x$ and $+2x$ give $-x$, the middle term of the given expression.

Example 2.14. $6x^2 - 13x + 6 = (3x - 2)(2x - 3)$

Example 2.15. $8x^2 - 14x - 15 = (4x + 3)(2x - 5)$

Example 2.16. $5x^2 - 15x = 5x(x - 3)$

Example 2.17. $9x^2 + 12x + 4 = (3x + 2)(3x + 2)$

Example 2.18. $x^2 - 10x + 25 = (x - 5)(x - 5)$

In the last two examples, in which the factors are alike, the original expressions are said to be perfect squares.

2.3   Quadratic equations; factor method

If a quadratic expression has a given value, i.e., it becomes an equation, the solution can often be found by the use of factors.

Consider

$$x^2 - x - 4 = 2$$
$$\therefore x^2 - x - 6 = 0$$
$$\therefore (x - 3)(x + 2) = 0$$

At this stage, the particular use of zero on the r.h.s. can be explained. On the l.h.s., we have two factors whose product is zero; this result can only be reached if one of the factors is itself equal to zero.

Compare $7 \times 0 = 0$ or $0 \times 5 = 0$.

From $\qquad (x - 3)(x + 2) = 0$

either $\qquad (x - 3) = 0 \quad$ or $\quad (x + 2) = 0$

$$\therefore x = 3 \quad \text{or} \quad x = -2$$

Thus we have two possible solutions to a quadratic equation.

Example 2.19. Solve $3x^2 - 12x = 0$.

$$3x^2 - 12x = 0$$
$$\therefore 3x(x - 4) = 0$$
$$\therefore \text{either } 3x = 0 \quad \text{or} \quad (x - 4) = 0$$
$$\therefore x = 0 \quad \text{or} \qquad x = 4$$

Note the effect if the original equation is divided by $3x$:

$$\frac{3x^2 - 12x}{3x} = 0$$
$$\therefore x - 4 = 0$$
$$\therefore x = 4$$

The process of dividing an equation by a term containing the variable cannot be valid unless we allow $x = 0$ to be one solution.

Example 2.20. Solve $x^2 - 6x + 9 = 0$.

$$x^2 - 6x + 9 = 0$$
$$\therefore (x - 3)(x - 3) = 0$$
$$\therefore x = 3 \text{ or } 3$$

Two identical solutions have a special significance in the graphical study of quadratic expressions and equations in a later paragraph.

Example 2.21. Solve $15x^2 - 14x - 8 = 0$.

$$15x^2 - 14x - 8 = 0$$
$$\therefore (5x + 2)(3x - 4) = 0$$
$$\therefore \text{ either } 5x + 2 = 0 \quad \text{or} \quad 3x - 4 = 0$$
$$\therefore 5x = -2 \quad \text{or} \quad 3x = 4$$
$$\therefore x = -\tfrac{2}{5} \quad \text{or} \quad x = \tfrac{4}{3}$$

EXERCISE 2.1

In questions 1 to 6, calculate the value of the currents in each section of the given circuits.

1.

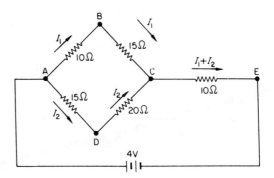

Fig. 2.3

2.

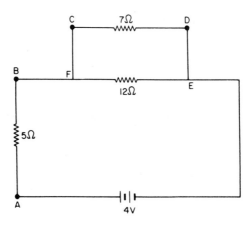

Fig. 2.4

3.

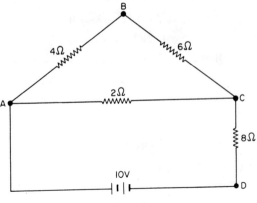

Fig. 2.5

4.

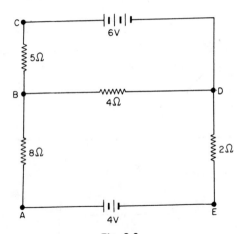

Fig. 2.6

5.

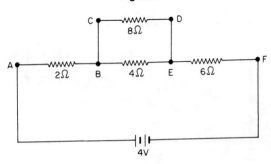

Fig. 2.7

6.

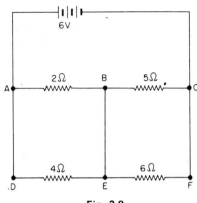

Fig. 2.8

7. A bridge network ABCD is arranged as follows; resistances between terminals A–B, B–C, C–D, D–A, and B–D are 10, 20, 15, 5, and 40 ohms respectively. A 20 V battery of negligible internal resistance is connected between terminals A and C. Determine the current in each resistor.

E.M.E.U.

8. Calculate the value of the current in each of the resistors shown in Fig. 2.9.

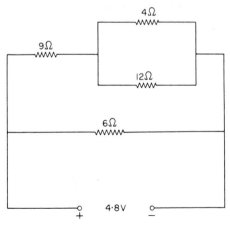

Fig. 2.9

Explain, without detailed calculation, why a break of continuity in the 12 ohm resistor will cause the current to fall in the 9 ohm resistor and rise in the 4 ohm resistor.

C.G.L.I. T.T.

9. (a) Calculate the value of the current I_1 for the junction shown in Fig. 2.10(a).

(b) For the circuit shown in Fig. 2.10(b), write down the potential difference between points X and Y, between points X and Z, and between points Y and Z, stating in each case which point is positive with respect to the other. Calculate the values of the currents I_2 and I_3, and also the value of the resistance R.

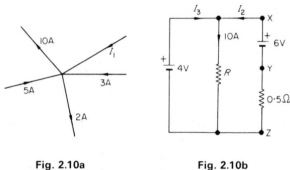

Fig. 2.10a   Fig. 2.10b

C.G.L.I. E.T.

10. (a) Calculate, using Kirchhoff's junction law, the current flowing in each branch of the circuit shown in Fig. 2.11. Show clearly the direction of current flow in each of the unmarked sections shown.

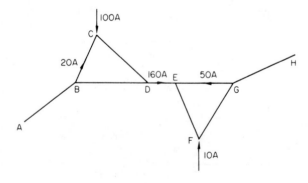

Fig. 2.11

(b) Calculate, using Kirchhoff's mesh law, the power supplied to the load in Fig. 2.12 if this load has a resistance of 4Ω.

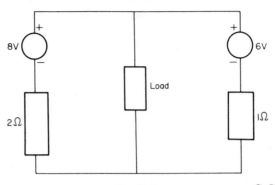

Fig. 2.12   C.G.L.I. E.T.

11. Six resistors are connected as shown in Fig. 2.13. If a battery having
    e.m.f. of 24 V and internal resistance of 1 Ω is connected to termi-
    nals A and B, calculate:

    (a) the current from the battery
    (b) the p.d. across the 8 Ω and the 4 Ω resistors,
    (c) the current taken from the battery if a conductor of negligible
        resistance is connected in parallel with the 8 Ω resistor.

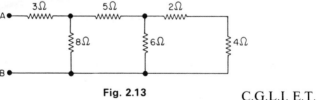

Fig. 2.13   C.G.L.I. E.T.

12. Two batteries, having internal resistances of 0·1 Ω and 0·12 Ω
    respectively, and each having an e.m.f. of 12 V, are connected as
    shown in Fig. 2.14 to an 18 V d.c. supply of negligible internal
    resistance.

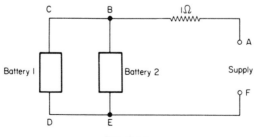

Fig. 2.14

(a) Re-draw the circuit showing conventional symbols and clearly showing polarities.

(b) Calculate the current taken by each battery and from the supply.

C.G.L.I. E.T.

13. State Kirchhoff's laws applying to the conditions between currents and voltages in the constituent parts of a resistive network containing sources of e.m.f. A Wheatstone Bridge network, having the circuit shown in Fig. 2.15, is set up to measure a resistance x. It is balanced when P is 45 ohms.

The ratio arms of 30 and 60 ohms are now interchanged in value. Calculate the resulting current that will flow in the 100 ohm galvanometer. Assume that the internal resistance of the 4 volt battery is negligible.

Fig. 2.15

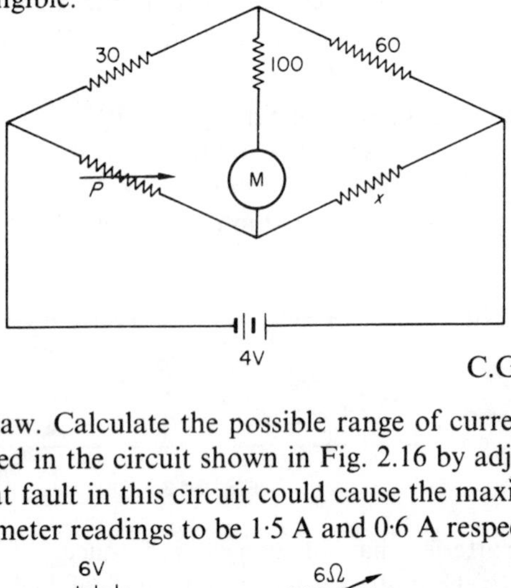

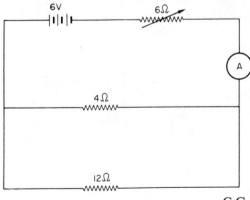

C.G.L.I. T.T.

14. State Ohm's law. Calculate the possible range of currents which can be obtained in the circuit shown in Fig. 2.16 by adjusting the rheostat. What fault in this circuit could cause the maximum and minimum ammeter readings to be 1·5 A and 0·6 A respectively?

Fig. 2.16

C.G.L.I. T.T.

15. State Ohm's law. Calculate the potential difference across terminals XY in Fig. 2.17 when the current in the 25 ohm resistor is 40 mA.

A battery of internal resistance 10 ohms is used to supply this circuit and in order to give the calculated potential difference across XY, a 20 ohm resistor in series with the battery is needed. What is the e.m.f. of this battery?

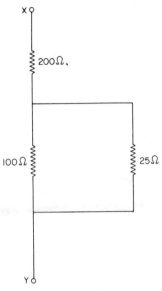

Fig. 2.17   C.G.L.I. T.T.

16. Solve for I_1 and I_2, giving answers to one decimal place:

$$0 \cdot 2I_1 + 0 \cdot 5(I_1 - 2) - 0 \cdot 2I_2 = 0$$
$$0 \cdot 2(I_1 - I_2) - 0 \cdot 5(I_1 + I_2 - 6) - 0 \cdot 2I_2 = 0$$

Y.C. (part Qn.)

17. Determine the values of V_1 and V_2, given that,

$$5V_1 + 12V_2 = 36 \cdot 1$$
$$11V_1 + 8V_2 = 37 \cdot 1$$

C.G.L.I. E.T. (part Qn.)

18. Currents I_1 and I_2 in a network are related by the equations,

$$2I_1 + 7I_2 = 36 \cdot 1$$
$$3I_1 + 6I_2 = 33 \cdot 9$$

Solve these simultaneous equations to obtain the values of I_1 and I_2.

C.G.L.I. E.T. (part Qn.)

19. Solve the following simultaneous equations for I_1 and I_2:

$$0{\cdot}05I_1 + 1(I_1 + I_2) = 2{\cdot}05$$
$$0{\cdot}08I_2 + 2(I_1 + I_2) = 4{\cdot}30$$

E.M.E.U.

20. The currents x and y in a certain circuit are connected by the following simultaneous equations:

$$0{\cdot}4x - 0{\cdot}3y = 3$$
$$1{\cdot}1x - 0{\cdot}2y = 5$$

Find x and y.   U.E.I. (part Qn.)

EXERCISE 2.2

Factorize the following expressions:

1. $3a^2b - 15b^2$
2. $4x^2 - 25y^2$
3. $2ab + 4ac + 3db + 6dc$
4. $5xy - 15xz + y - 3z$
5. $a^2 + ab - ca - cb$
6. $1 - 9c^2$
7. $2p^2 - 98q^2$
8. $3 \sin A \cos A - \sin^2 A$
9. $2 \tan^2 B + \tan B$
10. $1 - t^2 - a + at$
11. $4(b + c)^2 - 49(c + d)^2$
12. $a^3 - a$
13. $x^2 + 4x + 3$
14. $a^2 - 6a + 8$
15. $b^2 - 2b - 24$
16. $y^2 + 3y - 40$
17. $c^2 + 5c - 6$
18. $c^2 - 5c + 6$
19. $6x^2 + 5x - 4$
20. $10 - 7x - 12x^2$
21. $6x^2 + 17x + 12$
22. $18 + 37x + 15x^2$
23. $a^2 + 12ab + 20b^2$
24. $20c^2 + 3cd - 35d^2$
25. $30b^2 - b - 42$

Solve the following equations:

26. $x^2 - 8x + 12 = 0$
27. $x^2 + 14x + 45 = 0$
28. $6x^2 - x - 1 = 0$
29. $6 - 11x - 10x^2 = 0$
30. $8 + 15x + 7x^2 = 0$
31. $18x^2 + 3x = 10$
32. $16x^2 - 15 = -14x$
33. $4x^2 = 20x - 25$
34. $2x^2 = 14x$
35. $(x + 2)(2x - 1) = 6x + 3$

2.4 Quadratic equations by the method of completing the square

If $x^2 = 9$, then

$$x = \pm\sqrt{9} = \pm 3$$

If $(x + 2)^2 = 16$, then

$$x + 2 = \pm\sqrt{16}$$
$$\therefore x + 2 = \pm 4$$
$$\therefore x = \pm 4 - 2$$
$$= 2 \text{ or } -6$$

In each example above, the degree of the quadratic equation, i.e., the level of its highest power, 2, has been reduced to the first power by the process of finding a square root; this gives us a solution for x.

If $x^2 + 6x = 3$, it is not immediately possible to find a square root of the l.h.s. A quantity which is a perfect square has two identical factors and the addition of a particular number to $x^2 + 6x$ will make this a perfect square.

Let the required number be N and suppose that it has factors $n \times n$. The expression is now $x^2 + 6x + N$ which will have factors $(x + n)(x + n)$, a perfect square.

$$\therefore x^2 + 6x + N = (x + n)(x + n)$$
$$\therefore x^2 + 6x + N = x^2 + 2nx + n^2$$
$$\therefore 6x = 2nx \quad \text{(since } N = n^2) \tag{2.7}$$
$$\therefore 3 = n \tag{2.8}$$
$$\therefore N = n^2 = 9 \tag{2.9}$$

The completed expression is $x^2 + 6x + 9$, having factors $(x + 3) \times (x + 3)$.

Returning to the equation $x^2 + 6x = 3$, we add 9 to both sides, i.e.,

$$x^2 + 6x + 9 = 3 + 9$$
$$\therefore (x + 3)(x + 3) = 12$$
$$\therefore (x + 3)^2 = 12$$

Taking the square roots of both sides,

$$x + 3 = \pm\sqrt{12}$$
$$\therefore x = \pm\sqrt{12} - 3$$
$$= \pm 3 \cdot 464 - 3$$
$$= 0 \cdot 464 \text{ or } - 6 \cdot 464$$

The means of calculating the number to be added to the given expression in order to 'complete the square', is shown in steps (2.7), (2.8), and (2.9) above.

(2.7) read the coefficient of the x term, i.e., 6
(2.8) divide it by 2, i.e., 3
(2.9) square the result, i.e., 9.

Example 2.22.

$x^2 - 8x$	add $(-4)^2$	becomes	$x^2 - 8x + 16$
$x^2 + 10x$	add $(+5)^2$	becomes	$x^2 + 10x + 25$
$x^2 - 3x$	add $(-\frac{3}{2})^2$	becomes	$x^2 - 3x + \frac{9}{4}$
$x^2 + 7x$	add $(+\frac{7}{2})^2$	becomes	$x^2 + 7x + \frac{49}{4}$

It will be noticed, that in each of the given expressions, the coefficient of x^2 is 1. This is a necessary condition for this method to be used.

Example 2.23. Solve $2x^2 - 16x = 5$ correct to two places of decimals.

$$2x^2 - 16x = 5$$

$$\therefore x^2 - 8x = \frac{5}{2}$$

$$\therefore x^2 - 8x + 16 = \frac{5}{2} + 16$$

$$\therefore (x - 4)^2 = \frac{5 + 32}{2} = \frac{37}{2}$$

$$\therefore x - 4 = \pm\sqrt{18\cdot5}$$

$$\therefore x = \pm4\cdot301 + 4$$

$$= 8\cdot301 \quad \text{or} \quad -0\cdot301$$

$$= 8\cdot30 \quad \text{or} \quad -0\cdot30$$

Example 2.24. Solve $3x^2 - 7x - 2 = 0$ correct to two places of decimals.

$$3x^2 - 7x = 2$$

$$\therefore x^2 - \frac{7}{3}x = \frac{2}{3}$$

$$\therefore x^2 - \frac{7}{3}x + \left(\frac{7}{6}\right)^2 = \frac{2}{3} + \frac{49}{36}$$

$$\therefore \left(x - \frac{7}{6}\right)^2 = \frac{24 + 49}{36} = \frac{73}{36}$$

$$\therefore \left(x - \frac{7}{6}\right) = \frac{\pm\sqrt{73}}{6}$$

$$\therefore x = \frac{\pm\sqrt{73}}{6} + \frac{7}{6}$$

$$= \frac{\pm 8 \cdot 544 + 7}{6}$$

$$= \frac{15 \cdot 544}{6} \quad \text{or} \quad \frac{-1 \cdot 544}{6}$$

$$= 2 \cdot 591 \quad \text{or} \quad -0 \cdot 257$$

$$= 2.59 \quad \text{or} \quad -0 \cdot 26$$

2.5 Quadratic equations; solution by formula

A general formula can be developed if the method of completing the square is applied to a quadratic equation which is representative of all such equations; this generalized form is written as $ax^2 + bx + c = 0$.

$$ax^2 + bx + c = 0$$

$$\therefore x^2 + \frac{b}{a}x + \frac{c}{a} = 0$$

$$\therefore x^2 + \frac{b}{a}x = -\frac{c}{a}$$

$$\therefore x^2 + \frac{b}{a}x + \left(\frac{b}{2a}\right)^2 = \frac{b^2}{4a^2} - \frac{c}{a}$$

$$\therefore \left(x + \frac{b}{2a}\right)^2 = \frac{b^2 - 4ac}{4a^2}$$

$$\therefore x + \frac{b}{2a} = \frac{\pm\sqrt{b^2 - 4ac}}{2a}$$

$$\therefore x = \frac{-b \pm \sqrt{b^2 - 4ac}}{2a}$$

In using this formula, great care must be taken with the signs of the values, a, b, and c.

Example 2.25. Solve $2x^2 - 5x - 4 = 0$ correct to two places of decimals.

Comparing $\qquad\qquad 2x^2 - 5x - 4 = 0$

with $\qquad\qquad\qquad ax^2 + bx + c = 0$

we obtain $\qquad\qquad a = 2, \quad b = -5, \quad c = -4$

$$x = \frac{-b \pm \sqrt{b^2 - 4ac}}{2a}$$

$$\therefore \; x = \frac{-(-5) \pm \sqrt{(-5)^2 - 4(2)(-4)}}{4} \qquad (2.10)$$

$$= \frac{+5 \pm \sqrt{25 + 32}}{4} \qquad (2.11)$$

$$= \frac{5 \pm \sqrt{57}}{4}$$

$$= \frac{5 \pm 7\cdot55}{4}$$

$$\therefore \; x = \frac{12\cdot55}{4} \quad \text{or} \quad \frac{-2\cdot55}{4}$$

$$= 3\cdot14 \quad \text{or} \quad -0\cdot64$$

In (2.10), the use of brackets is a safeguard in the correct evaluation of the term $-4ac$, resulting in $+32$ in (2.11). The expression, $b^2 - 4ac$, under the square root sign is called the 'discriminant' and of course must be positive for a real solution of x; it is possible for it to be zero, in which case the equation has two identical solutions.

EXERCISE 2.3

Solve questions 1 to 8 by the method of completing the square, and questions 9 to 16 by the formula; give answers correct to three significant figures where appropriate.

1. $x^2 - 14x + 7 = 0$
2. $x^2 + 5x - 2 = 0$

3. $2x^2 - 12x = 9$
4. $3x^2 + 11x = -8$
5. $7x = 2 - x^2$
6. $\dfrac{1}{(x + 2)} + \dfrac{1}{x} = \dfrac{3}{(x - 3)}$
7. $px^2 + 2qx + r = 0$
8. $mx^2 + nx - s = 0$
9. $x^2 + 5x + 3 = 0$
10. $4x^2 - 10x + 3 = 0$
11. $3x^2 + x - 5 = 0$
12. $5x^2 - 2x - 6 = 0$
13. $2{\cdot}5x^2 - 4{\cdot}2x - 1{\cdot}5 = 0$
14. $6 - 12{\cdot}8x = 3{\cdot}5x^2$
15. $2ax^2 + bx - c = 0$
16. $ax^2 + 2bx + c = 0$

2.6 Problems leading to quadratic equations

The important work in solving a problem is the analysis of the relations between the quantities which leads to the development of an equation. The solution of the equation usually falls into one of a few particular types, e.g., simultaneous or quadratic.

If there were a so-called 'standard method' of solving problems, these questions would cease to be problems. In general, the given quantities must be brought into close relation with the unknown quantities. The first step, therefore, is to assume a measurement, with stated dimensions, of the quantity to be found and to apply the conditions of the question to it.

Example 2.26. Two resistances in series total 30 Ω. The same resistances in parallel total 7·2 Ω. Calculate the value of each.

Let one resistance be R_1 Ω. Now let this assumed value become part of the question. If we know the value of one and the total of two resistances, then the difference gives us the value of the second.

$$\therefore \text{ the second resistance} = (30 - R_1)\,\Omega$$

Now read these two values into the remainder of the question, i.e., connect them in parallel.

$$\therefore \quad \frac{1}{R_1} + \frac{1}{(30 - R_1)} = \frac{1}{7{\cdot}2} = \frac{5}{36}$$

Multiply each term by $36R_1(30 - R_1)$,

$$\therefore\ 36R_1(30 - R_1)\frac{1}{R_1} + 36R_1(30 - R_1)\frac{1}{(30 - R_1)}$$

$$= 36R_1(30 - R_1)\frac{5}{36}$$

$$\therefore\ 36(30 - R_1) + 36R_1 = 5R_1(30 - R_1)$$

$$\therefore\ 1080 - 36R_1 + 36R_1 = 150R_1 - 5R_1{}^2$$

$$\therefore\ 5R_1{}^2 - 150R_1 + 1080 = 0$$

$$\therefore\ R_1{}^2 - 30R_1 + 216 = 0$$

$$\therefore\ (R_1 - 18)(R_1 - 12) = 0$$

$$\therefore\ R_1 = 18\ \text{or}\ 12$$

One resistance is 18 Ω and the other 12 Ω.

Example 2.27. Four quadrants of equal radii are cut from the corners of a square metal plate to produce the shape shown in the diagram. Find the length of the original plate if the final area is 36 cm². Use $\pi = \frac{22}{7}$ and give the answer correct to three significant figures.

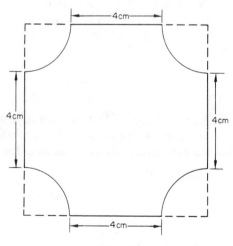

Fig. 2.18

Let the radius of each quadrant be r cm

$$\therefore \text{ side of square} = (4 + 2r) \text{ cm}$$
$$\therefore \text{ area of square} = (4 + 2r)^2 \text{ cm}^2$$

The four quadrants together make the area of one circle.

$$\therefore (4 + 2r)^2 - \pi r^2 = 36$$

$$\therefore (4 + 2r)(4 + 2r) - \frac{22r^2}{7} = 36$$

$$\therefore 16 + 8r + 8r + 4r^2 - \frac{22r^2}{7} = 36$$

Multiply through by 7,

$$\therefore 112 + 56r + 56r + 28r^2 - 22r^2 = 252$$
$$\therefore 6r^2 + 112r + 112 - 252 = 0$$
$$\therefore 6r^2 + 112r - 140 = 0$$
$$\therefore 3r^2 + 56r - 70 = 0$$

Using the method of the formula, $a = 3$, $b = 56$, and $c = -70$.

$$\therefore r = \frac{-56 \pm \sqrt{56^2 - 4(3)(-70)}}{6}$$

$$= \frac{-56 \pm \sqrt{3136 + 840}}{6}$$

$$= \frac{-56 \pm \sqrt{3976}}{6}$$

$$= \frac{-56 \pm 63 \cdot 05}{6}$$

$$= \frac{7 \cdot 05}{6} \quad \text{or} \quad -\frac{119 \cdot 05}{6}$$

The negative answer is impractical; hence $r = 1 \cdot 18$ cm, correct to three significant figures. Hence length of plate = $6 \cdot 36$ cm.

Example 2.28. Determine the diameters of two circles such that one circle has a radius 1 cm greater than the other and an area double that of the other.

Let the radius of the smaller circle be r cm, then the radius of the larger is $(r + 1)$ cm.

$$\therefore \; \pi(r + 1)^2 = 2\pi r^2$$

$$\therefore \; (r + 1)^2 = 2r^2$$

$$\therefore \; (r + 1)(r + 1) = 2r^2$$

$$\therefore \; r^2 + 2r + 1 = 2r^2$$

$$\therefore \; 0 = r^2 - 2r - 1$$

Using the formula, $a = 1, b = -2, c = -1$.

$$\therefore \; r = \frac{-(-2) \pm \sqrt{(-2)^2 - 4(1)(-1)}}{2}$$

$$= \frac{2 \pm \sqrt{4 + 4}}{2}$$

$$= \frac{2 \pm \sqrt{8}}{2}$$

$$= \frac{2 \pm 2 \cdot 828}{2}$$

$$= \frac{4 \cdot 828}{2} \quad \text{or} \quad \frac{-0 \cdot 828}{2}$$

The negative solution is impractical; hence $r = 2 \cdot 414$ cm., and diameters $= 4 \cdot 828$ cm and $5 \cdot 828$ cm

EXERCISE 2.4

1. A rectangular piece of copper of area 50 cm^2 is to be cut from a large sheet. Its length must be 2 cm more than its breadth. If the breadth is x cm, form a quadratic equation in x and hence find the dimensions of the piece of copper correct to two decimal places. Five of these pieces, each 0·1 cm thick, weigh 221 g. What is the density of copper used?   Y.C. (part Qn.)

2. The Weston cell is used as a standard e.m.f. of 1·0183 V at 20°C. The e.m.f. varies with temperature in such a way that if the temperature is $(20 + x)°C$, the correction is $-(x^2 + 41x) \cdot 10^{-6}$ V. Calculate the temperature at which a correction of $-0 \cdot 000510$ V is required, assuming only the positive answer is valid.

3. A solid cylinder has a total surface area of 100π cm². Calculate the radius if its length is 8 cm. Give your answer correct to three significant figures.

4. An arch has the dimensions shown in the diagram. Calculate the rise R m if the radius r is 10 m and the span S is 12 m given that,

$$r = \frac{1}{2}\left[\frac{(\frac{1}{2}S)^2}{R} + R\right]$$

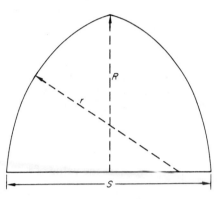

Fig. 2.19

5. A particle travels a distance s metres in t, seconds, given by $s = ut + \frac{1}{2}ft^2$. Calculate how long it will take to travel 100 m, given that $u = 10$ m/s and $f = 32$ m/s².

6. The diagonal of a rectangle is 15 cm in length and the long side is 3 cm longer than the short side. Calculate the dimensions of the rectangle.

7. A locking device is in the shape of an annulus with a piece of metal removed which can be regarded as rectangular.

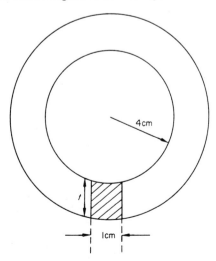

If the internal radius is 4 cm and the area of metal is 10 cm², calculate the value of t assuming it to be the difference between the radii.

8. The total surface area of a cone is 400π cm² and its slant height is 50 cm. Calculate the radius.

9. Two metal spheres of different material have the same mass, 10 g. Their volumes differ by 15 cm³ and their densities by 1·2 g/ml. Calculate their volumes.

10. A certain number of telegraph poles are used to support 2 km of wire. If the route could be shortened to $1\frac{1}{2}$ km, there would be a saving of 10 poles and the distance would be 2·5 m shorter between consecutive poles. Calculate the original distance between consecutive poles.

11. A circle of radius r cm is described in a quadrant of another circle of radius 10 cm. Calculate the value of r.

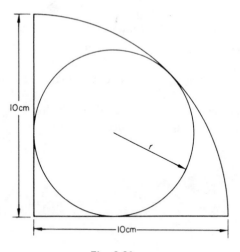

Fig. 2.21

12. A metal plate is in the shape of an isosceles triangle with a semi-circle attached, as in Fig. 2.22. The total area of the plate is 250 cm². Calculate the radius of the semicircle.

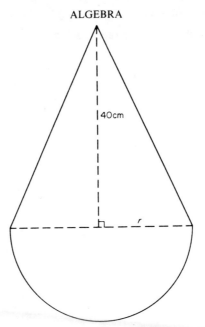

Fig. 2.22

13. Figure 2.23 shows the cross-section of a warehouse 25 m long and volume 1700 m³. It is in the form of a rectangle with a semicircle described outwards on its upper shorter side. The greatest height is 12 m. Show that the width of the warehouse, 2x m, is given by the equation,

$$(4 - \pi)x^2 - 48x + 136 = 0$$

Hence find the width of the warehouse, correct to two decimal places.

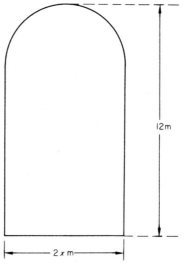

Fig. 2.23

U.E.I.

14. In Fig. 2.24, show that the radius R is a root of the equation,

$$2R^2 - 12R + 13 = 0$$

Determine R correct to three significant figures.

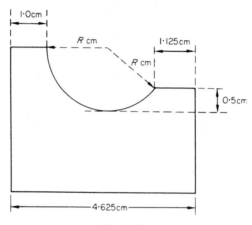

Fig. 2.24 U.E.I.

15. The relationship between grid voltage V_g and anode current i_a of a valve in a square-law modulator is found to be;

$$i_a = V_g{}^2 + 18 \cdot 2V_g + 82 \cdot 81$$

where V_g is in volts and i_a is in mA. At what grid voltage will the valve 'cut off' (i.e., i_a become zero)? What will be the potential on the grid when $i_a = 40$ mA?

2.7 Quadratic equations; solution by graph

The essential difference between a function and an equation has been referred to in Vol. 1: the importance of this justifies its repetition. A functional relationship between two variables shows a series of continuous values, each conforming to the same pattern.

If $y = x^2$, and x takes the values 1, 2, 3, etc., then y takes the values 1, 4, 9, etc.

An equation shows a relationship which is true for only particular values of the variables. If $x^2 = 9$, then $x = +3$ or -3 and no other values.

We can think of an equation as being one definite position on the corresponding function. Since a function of two variables can be constructed as a graph, the solution of equations which depend on that function is a matter of finding the correct position on the graph.

Example 2.29. Solve $x^2 + 2x - 3 = 0$ graphically, given that the solutions lie between -4 and $+2$.

For each integral value of x, we find the corresponding value of y and tabulate the results.

$$y = x^2 + 2x - 3$$

x	-4	-3	-2	-1	0	1	2
x^2	16	9	4	1	0	1	4
$+2x$	-8	-6	-4	-2	0	2	4
-3	-3	-3	-3	-3	-3	-3	-3
y	5	0	-3	-4	-3	0	5

It should be noted that the values of y in the last line are symmetrical about the value -4; in this case it can be assumed that -4 is the lowest value of y on the graph. Symmetry of y values is frequently noticeable in the table, but not always about a single point. If the y values are 4, 0, -2, -2, 0, 4, then the lowest value of y on the graph is half-way in position between the two symmetrically lowest values, -2, -2.

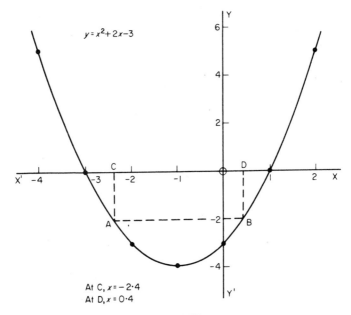

At C, $x = -2 \cdot 4$
At D, $x = 0 \cdot 4$

Fig. 2.25

There are other occasions when the table of values of a quadratic function shows no symmetry in the y values, but it is important to remember that all graphs of quadratic functions are symmetrical; the name parabola is given to these graphs.

Figure 2.25 shows the result of plotting the values in the table. Only individual practice will give the skill required to achieve a smooth curve. The following suggestions will be of some assistance.

(a) Avoid drawing from point to point.

(b) Draw from a position on the inside of the curve where the freedom of wrist movement provides a natural radius.

(c) Draw through as many points as possible in one movement, especially near the lowest or highest value of y; this prevents the turning point from being too sharp or too flat.

(d) The arms of the parabola soon become almost straight and, in general, less important than the remainder of the curve.

To solve $x^2 + 2x - 3 = 0$ graphically.

We regard the graph as a measuring instrument and make the following comparison,

$$x^2 + 2x - 3 = y$$
$$x^2 + 2x - 3 = 0$$

The equation coincides with the graph where $y = 0$. The solutions to the equation can be found on the graph where $y = 0$, i.e., where the graph cuts the x-axis, at $x = -3$ and $x = 1$.

Example 2.30. Using the same graph, solve the equation,

$$x^2 + 2x - 1 = 0$$

Compare $x^2 + 2x - 3 = y$

and $x^2 + 2x - 1 = 0$

Adjust the equation to coincide with the graph:

$$x^2 + 2x - 1 - 2 = -2$$
$$\therefore \ x^2 + 2x - 3 = -2$$

Equation and graph now coincide where $y = -2$. Draw AB through $y = -2$ to cut the graph at A and B; draw from A and B, perpendiculars AC and BD to the x-axis. The x values of the positions C and D are the required solutions.

Example 2.31. Using the same graph, solve the equation, $x^2 + x - 3 = 0$.

Compare $\qquad\qquad x^2 + 2x - 3 = y \qquad$ (graph)

and $\qquad\qquad\qquad x^2 + x - 3 = 0 \qquad$ (equation)

Adjust the equation to coincide with the graph:

$$x^2 + x + x - 3 = x \qquad \text{(equation)}$$
$$\therefore\ x^2 + 2x - 3 = x \qquad \text{(equation)}$$
$$x^2 + 2x - 3 = y \qquad \text{(graph)}$$

Equation and graph now coincide where $y = x$. This solution differs from Examples 2.29, 2.30 in that y is no longer a constant but a new graph, a straight line through the origin having the equation $y = x$. Plot three convenient points and join with a straight line; the intersection of this line with the curve gives the required solutions measured on the x-axis.

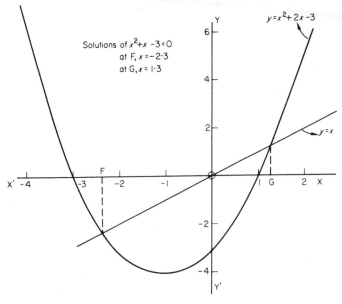

Fig. 2.26

Example 2.32. Solve graphically, $4 - 3x - x^2 = 0$, given that the solutions lie between -5 and $+2$.

Construct a table of values for drawing the corresponding graph, $y = 4 - 3x - x^2$.

$$y = 4 - 3x - x^2$$

x	-5	-4	-3	-2	-1	0	1	2
4	4	4	4	4	4	4	4	4
$-3x$	15	12	9	6	3	0	-3	-6
$-x^2$	-25	-16	-9	-4	-1	0	-1	-4
y	-6	0	4	6	6	4	0	-6

Note the following features of the function and the values of y;

(a) the sign of the highest power in the function is now negative,

(b) the values of y indicate that the graph is reversed in shape compared with Example 2.29,

(c) there are two symmetrically highest values of y, 6 and 6; the maximum value of y lies half-way in position between these values, i.e., where $x = -1\frac{1}{2}$. For accuracy of drawing, this value could be calculated ($y = 6\frac{1}{4}$) and plotted.

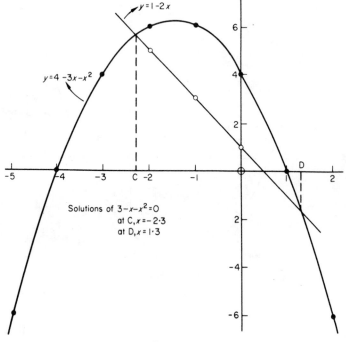

Fig. 2.27

From the equation to be solved, $4 - 3x - x^2 = 0$, we note that the solutions are to be found where $y = 0$, i.e., where the graph cuts the x-axis at $x = -4$ and $+1$.

Using the same graph, solve $3 - x - x^2 = 0$.

At first sight, this equation bears no relation to the graph; it can be made to fit on the graph by adjustment.

$$\text{Compare} \qquad 4 - 3x - x^2 = y \qquad \text{(graph)}$$
$$\text{and} \qquad 3 - x - x^2 = 0 \qquad \text{(equation)}$$
$$\text{adding} \quad \frac{1 - 2x \qquad\qquad 1 - 2x}{4 - 3x - x^2 = 1 - 2x}$$

Hence the equation coincides with the graph where $y = 1 - 2x$. Draw this new graph to intersect the parabola and read off the x values of the points of intersection at C and D in Fig. 2.27. Thus, $x = -2\cdot3$ and $+1\cdot3$ are the solutions of the equation $3 - x - x^2 = 0$.

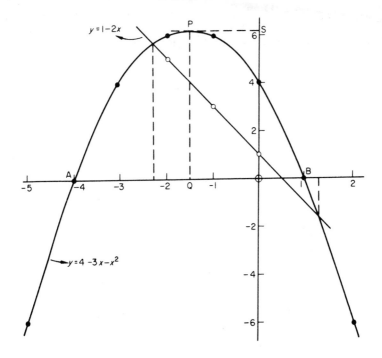

Fig. 2.28

Other questions solved graphically.

1. For what value of x is $4 - 3x - x^2$ a maximum?
2. What is the maximum value of $4 - 3x - x^2$?
3. For what range of values of x is $4 - 3x - x^2$ greater than $1 - 2x$?

For each of these above questions, we repeat the graph of the previous example. (See Fig. 2.28.)

1. Find the turning point P on the graph and read off the x value at Q, i.e., $-1\frac{1}{2}$. This position is always the mid-point of the length AB, thus showing PQ to be an axis of symmetry of the parabola.
2. The maximum value of $4 - 3x - x^2$ is the maximum value of y to be read along the y-axis at S, i.e., $6\frac{1}{4}$.
3. The question could be read as, 'over what range of values of x does the curve stand higher than the line, $y = 1 - 2x$?' This will be true for all values of x lying between the points of intersection of the curve and the line, i.e., from $x = -2 \cdot 3$ to $x = +1 \cdot 3$.

Example 2.33. The equation $x^2 - 4x + 4 = 0$ has two identical solutions, $x = 2$ or 2. Draw the graph of the corresponding function, $y = x^2 - 4x + 4$ between the values of $x = 0$ and $x = 4$, and interpret the meaning of the identical solutions.

$$y = x^2 - 4x + 4$$

x	0	1	2	3	4
y	4	1	0	1	4

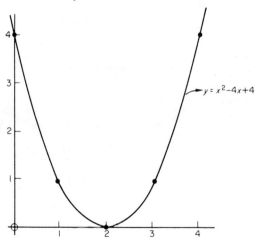

Fig. 2.29

The function, $x^2 - 4x + 4$, having two identical factors $(x - 2) \times (x - 2)$, is a perfect square, $(x - 2)^2$. Hence, for all values of x, the function is positive and the corresponding graph must remain above the x-axis. Since the graph has only one point of contact with the x-axis, at $x = 2$, it is tangential to the axis at this point.

EXERCISE 2.5

1. Draw the graph of $y = x^2 - 4x$ for values of x from -1 to $+5$. Hence solve from your graph:

   (a) $x^2 - 4x = 0$ (b) $x^2 - 4x = -2$.

2. Draw the graph of $y = 5x - x^2$ for values of x from -1 to $+6$. Hence solve from your graph:

   (a) $5x - x^2 = 0$ (b) $5x - x^2 = 3{\cdot}5$.

3. Draw the graph of $y = x^2 + 3x - 4$ for values of x from -5 to $+2$. Hence solve:

   (a) $x^2 + 3x - 4 = 0$ (b) $x^2 + 3x - 2 = 0$.

4. A cable suspended from two pylons 100 m apart, takes the form of the curve, $y = x^2/100 + 45$ where y is the height in metres above the ground of a point P on the cable, and x is the horizontal distance in metres of P from the lowest point of the cable. Plot the curve from $x = -50$ to $x = +50$ at intervals of 10. From the graph, find,

   (a) the clearance of the cable from the ground,
   (b) the heights of the supports if the cable spans 84 m but takes the same form,
   (c) the distance between supports to give a maximum sag of 5 m.

   U.E.I.

5. Draw the graph of $y = x^2 - 3x - 2$ for values of x from -2 to $+5$. What is the minimum value of y? Use your graph to find two values of x, in each case, such that,

   (a) $x^2 - 3x - 2 = 0$ (b) $x^2 - 3x - 4 = 0$

   U.E.I.

6. Plot the graph of $y = x^2 - 5x + 4$ for values of x from 0 to 6. On the same graph paper and using the same axes, draw the graph, $x - y = 2$. What are the co-ordinates of the points of intersection of the two graphs?

   U.E.I.

7. Plot the two graphs, $y = x^2 - 4$ and $y = x - 2$ over the range, $x = 3$ to $x = -3$. Use the same graph paper and the same scales. From the graphs state,

(a) the values of x and y at the points where the graphs cross,
(b) the values of x which make $y = 0$ for each graph.

U.L.C.I.

8. Plot the graph of $y = x^2 + x - 6$ between the values $x = 4$ and $x = -4$. From the graph, find the value of y when $x = -\frac{1}{2}$. Use the graph to solve the equation, $x^2 + x - 6 = 0$.

U.L.C.I.

9. (a) Using the same axes, draw the graphs of $y_1 = 15 + 17x - 4x^2$ between $x = -1$ and $x = +5$, and that of $y_2 = 15/x$ between $x = \frac{1}{2}$ and $x = 5$.

(b) State, (i) the values of x where $y_1 = y_2$, (ii) the values of x between which $y_2 < y_1$.

(c) Write in a simplified form the equation of which the results of (b)(i) are the roots.

C.G.L.I. T.T.

10. A sector of a circle radius r contains an angle θ radians at the centre of the circle. If the total perimeter of the sector is 12 m, find a formula connecting r and θ and show that the area A of the sector is given by $A = 6r - r^2$. Find with the aid of a graph, the maximum value of A, and the values of r and θ corresponding to this maximum.

C.G.L.I. T.T.

11. A solid cylinder is such that its height plus its girth is 9π cm. Find an expression for its total surface area in terms of radius r and hence by a graphical method find the value of r, between 0 and 5 cm, which makes the area a maximum value. From this value of r, calculate the value of h.

12. A projectile rises to a height of h m in t s given by $h = 400t - 16t^2$. Draw a graph showing h and t for values of t from 0 to 25. From the graph, find,

(a) the maximum height to which the projectile rises,
(b) the time to the maximum height,
(c) the times at which the projectile is at a height of 1200 m.

13. The time of vibration of a compound pendulum is given by the formula,

$$T = 2\pi \sqrt{\left(\frac{k^2 + l^2}{lg}\right)}$$

where l is the distance of the point of support from the centre of gravity. If $k = 2 \cdot 5$ and $g = 32$, calculate the values of T for values of l between 0 and 5. Draw a graph connecting T with l and thus determine the value of l when T is a minimum.   U.E.I.

14. An arch as shown in the Fig. 2.30 has a height h m at a distance x m from A, given by

$$h = 4 + \sqrt{(16 + 6x - x^2)}$$

Draw a graph for values of x from 0 to 6 m and from it find the maximum height of the arch.

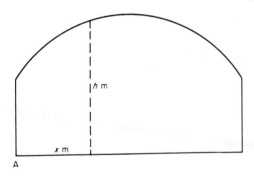

Fig. 2.30

15. Two radii, OA and OB of a circle radius 10 cm, are rotating in directions as shown in Fig. 2.31. Show that the area of the $\triangle OAB$ is given by

$$\frac{b}{2}\sqrt{\left(100 - \frac{b^2}{4}\right)}$$

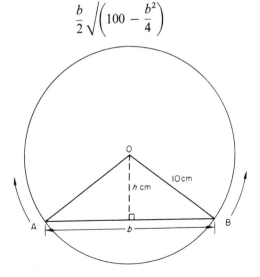

Fig. 2.31

Draw a graph showing the area of the $\triangle OAB$ and base b, for values of b from 10 cm to 18 cm. From your graph find,

(a) the value of b which gives the maximum area of $\triangle OAB$,
(b) the maximum area of $\triangle OAB$,
(c) the values of b for which the area of $\triangle OAB$ is 45·5 cm².

3. Algebra

3.1 Variation; proportion

We have referred to the measurements used to plot graphs as 'variables';
x the independent variable and y the dependent variable. It is clear that
in drawing one graph, we can illustrate the relation between two
variables only. In practice, using the dimensions frequently met with in
the laboratory and workshop, it is rarely that we find such a simple
relationship containing only two variables. Let us suppose that our
problem involves three variables, current I, voltage V, and resistance
R. In order to study their variation, we shall need to keep one of them
constant and observe values of the other two.

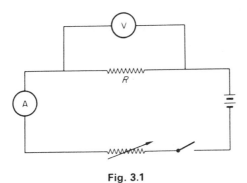

Fig. 3.1

The circuit shown in Fig. 3.1 will allow us to measure a variable current
flowing through the resistance R and at the same time observe the p.d.
across the ends of R. If these results are drawn as a graph, with current

on the horizontal axis and p.d. on the vertical axis, a straight-line graph would result.

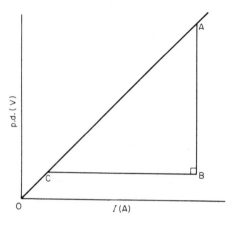

Fig. 3.2

The conclusion to be drawn from this graph is that the p.d. across a conductor is directly proportional to the current flowing through it. We infer from chapter 8 of Vol. 1 that only first powers of the variables are concerned in this relationship; we write p.d. $\propto I$. This was first stated as Ohm's law, though in reverse manner, i.e., the current flowing in a conductor is directly proportional to the p.d. between the ends of the conductor; the two statements are equivalent. In Vol. 1 we were able to determine from a straight-line graph the form of its equation by consideration of its gradient and intercept; in our experiment the intercept is zero. From the gradient AB/BC, which is constant along the whole length of the line, we can formulate the relation,

$$\text{p.d.} = k \times I \tag{3.1}$$

$$\therefore \frac{\text{p.d.}}{I} = k$$

By definition and by a suitable choice of units, this value k is the resistance R ohm of the conductor.

Thus
$$\frac{V}{I} = R \tag{3.2}$$

or
$$I = \frac{V}{R} \tag{3.3}$$

If now we carry out a further series of observations with a circuit in which V is constant and we observe the currents through different resistances, the graph of I (vertical axis) and R (horizontal axis) will no longer be a straight line but as shown in Fig. 3.3.

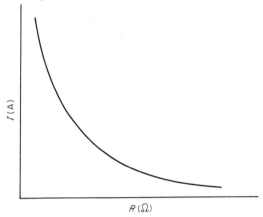

Fig. 3.3

From the graph, and the function (3.3), $I = V/R$, i.e., $I = $ a constant$/R$, it can be seen that as R increases, I will decrease and vice versa. This type of relationship is known as inverse proportion, for which we write $I \propto 1/R$. The sign of proportionality, $\propto$, is to be regarded as a general description of the way in which two variables behave. It does not have the exactness of an equals sign. It is, however, only a small step from one to the other; thus if p.d. $\propto I$, then p.d. $= k \times I$ and if $I \propto 1/R$, then $I = c \times 1/R$.

It is now possible to combine these two functions. We could say that I is directly proportional to V and inversely proportional to R.

$$\therefore \ I \propto \frac{V}{R}, \qquad \therefore \ I = k\frac{V}{R}$$

This is Ohm's law and the definition of the units, ampere, volt, and ohm have been made so as to make $k = 1$.

Example 3.1. In a test of a tangent galvanometer, the following values of the deflection θ and the current I were obtained.

I (amp)	0·06	0·14	0·18	0·26	0·30
θ (degrees)	12	25	31	41	45

Draw a graph showing the relation between I and $\tan \theta$ and determine the equation in the form $I = k \tan \theta$ where k is a constant. U.L.C.I.

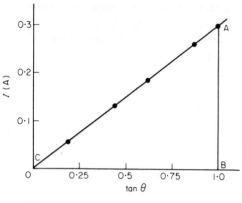

Fig. 3.4

$$\frac{AB}{BC} = \text{gradient} = \frac{0.3}{1} = k$$

Hence $$I = 0.3 \tan \theta$$

Therefore, I is directly proportional to $\tan \theta$.

Example 3.2. We are required to find the relationship between the cross-sectional area of a wire and its resistance; these dimensions then are our variables, all other possible effects, length of wire, temperature, and material of wire, must be maintained constant. The following observations were made by experiment.

S.W.G.	12	14	16	18	20	22	24
$A(\text{mm}^2)$	5.48	3.23	2.09	1.17	0.655	0.396	0.245
$R(\Omega/\text{m})$	0.003	0.005	0.008	0.015	0.026	0.043	0.070

The results, drawn as a graph, are shown in Fig. 3.5.

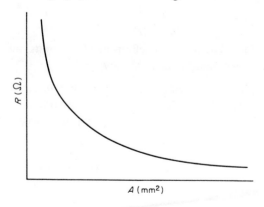

Fig. 3.5

The shape of this graph is similar to that in Fig. 3.3 which suggests that R is inversely proportional to A, i.e.,

$$R \propto \frac{1}{A}, \quad \text{or} \quad R = k\left(\frac{1}{A}\right)$$

We could confirm this possible result, if in this last equation we regarded $1/A$ as the variable to be plotted.

A (mm^2)	5·48	3·23	2·09	1·17	0·655	0·396	0·245
$1/A$	0·182	0·31	0·48	0·86	1·53	2·52	4·08
R (ohm/m)	0·003	0·005	0·008	0·015	0·026	0·043	0·070

The results as a graph are shown in Fig. 3.6.

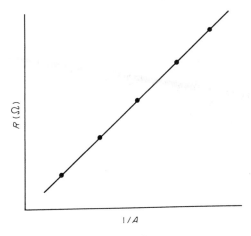

Fig. 3.6

Since the graph is a straight line, we can say that R is directly proportional to $1/A$. Hence $R \propto 1/A$, which confirms our original supposition that R is inversely proportional to A. If the conditions of a problem compel us to consider three or more variables, then a method of calculation is necessary. The principles of direct and inverse proportion are still required and it becomes necessary to find the value of the constant k, which links proportionality with equality, i.e., it converts a statement into an equation.

Example 3.3. The capacitance C of a plate condenser is directly proportional to the area A of the plates and inversely proportional to the distance d between them. If $C = 0.000125$ mF when $A = 60$ cm^2 and

$d = 0.12$ cm, find C when $A = 150$ cm^2 and $d = 0.09$ cm. Give the answer correct to three significant figures.

N.C.T.E.C. (part Qn.)

Statement, $$C \propto \frac{A}{d}$$

Equation, $$C = k\frac{A}{d}$$

$$\therefore \ 0.000125 = k\frac{60}{0.12}$$

$$= 500k$$

$$\therefore \ k = \frac{0.000125}{500} = 2.5 \times 10^{-7}$$

Substituting in the equation, $C = k\dfrac{A}{d}$

$$C = \frac{2.5 \times 10^{-7}A}{d}$$

If $A = 150$ cm^2 and $d = 0.09$ cm,

$$\therefore \ C = \frac{2.5 \times 10^{-7} \times 150}{0.09}$$

$$\therefore \ C = 4.17 \times 10^{-4} \ \text{mF}$$

Example 3.4. (a) The resistance R of a wire is proportional to its length l, and inversely proportional to the square of its diameter, d. (b) The weight W of the wire is proportional to the product of its length and the square of its diameter. (c) Express each of these statements in the form of an equation and use them to find a formula connecting R with W and l. (d) State how R varies with W and l. (e) The resistance of a certain telephone wire is 18 ohms per km and the weight of the wire is 23.7 kg per km. (f) Calculate the resistance of 5 km of the wire of the same material weighing 17 kg per km.

U.E.I.

Note. The sentences have been lettered for simplicity of discussion; they were not numbered in the examination paper from which the question was taken.

A question of this length should be re-read and analysed; punctuation is often very useful in showing the required stages of calculation.

In this case, the analysis falls into the consideration of complete sentences, hence the use of the letters.

(a) $R \propto \dfrac{l}{d^2}$, and (b) $W \propto ld^2$

(c) Convert statements (a) and (b) into equations by means of constants; use different constants.

$$\therefore \ R = \frac{kl}{d^2} \quad \text{and} \quad W = cld^2$$

A formula is required connecting R, W, and l; hence eliminate d.
  From $R = kl/d^2$,

$$d^2 = \frac{kl}{R}$$

From $W = cld^2$,

$$d^2 = \frac{W}{cl}$$

Hence
$$\frac{kl}{R} = \frac{W}{cl}$$

$$\therefore \ RW = kcl^2$$

$$\therefore \ R = \frac{kcl^2}{W}$$

The product of the two constants k and c will be another constant; let $kc = K$.

$$\therefore \ R = \frac{Kl^2}{W}$$

(d) Make a statement of proportionality by omitting K. Therefore R is directly proportional to the square of the length l and inversely proportional to the weight W.

(e) Introduce the given values to find the constant K.
  From $R = Kl^2/W$, substituting $R = 18$, $W = 23.7$ and $l = 1$,

$$18 = \frac{K.1^2}{23.7}$$

$$\therefore \ K = 18 \times 23.7$$

(f) Use this value of K in the equation, $R = Kl^2/W$

$$\therefore R = \frac{18 \times 23.7 \times 5^2}{17}$$

$$= 627\,\Omega \quad (S.R.)$$

An alternative wording to the use of the phrase 'is proportional to' is 'varies as'. Thus, the resistance of a wire varies directly as its length and inversely as the cross-sectional area.

Comparative values

It is often important to determine the change in a dependent variable, rather than to calculate a particular value. This change will depend on those occurring in the independent variables in which small variations may occur due to causes such as temperature, heat losses, impurities, instrument errors, etc. The variations can be expressed as percentage values or in the form of ratios.

Percentage change

The resistance of a wire varies directly as its length and inversely as the square of its diameter. If the length is increased by 5% and the diameter increased by 4%, calculate the percentage change in the resistance.

In general,

$$R \propto \frac{l}{d^2}, \qquad \therefore R = \frac{kl}{d^2}$$

In order to compare the two sets of measurements, attach suffixes 1 and 2 to each of the variables.

Thus,

$$R_1 = \frac{kl_1}{d_1^{\,2}} \quad \text{and} \quad R_2 = \frac{kl_2}{d_2^{\,2}} \tag{3.4}$$

Comparing lengths,

$$l_2 = \frac{105}{100}\,l_1 \qquad \therefore l_2 = \frac{21}{20}\,l_1$$

Comparing diameters,

$$d_2 = \frac{104}{100}\,d_1 \qquad \therefore d_2 = \frac{26}{25}\,d_1$$

From (3.4):
$$R_2 = \frac{k\left(\frac{21}{20}l_1\right)}{\left(\frac{26}{25}d_1\right)^2}$$

$$= \frac{kl_1\frac{21}{20}}{d_1{}^2\left(\frac{26}{25}\right)^2}$$

$$= \frac{kl_1}{d_1{}^2} \cdot \frac{21}{20} \cdot \left(\frac{25}{26}\right)^2$$

Percentage change $= \dfrac{\text{actual change}}{\text{original value}} \times \dfrac{100}{1}$

Therefore, percentage change in R is

$$\frac{R_2 - R_1}{R_1} \times \frac{100}{1} = \frac{\dfrac{kl_1}{d_1{}^2} \cdot \dfrac{21}{20} \cdot \left(\dfrac{25}{26}\right)^2 - \dfrac{kl_1}{d_1{}^2}}{\dfrac{kl_1}{d_1{}^2}} \times \frac{100}{1} \qquad (3.5)$$

$$= \frac{\left[\dfrac{21}{20} \cdot \left(\dfrac{25}{26}\right)^2 - 1\right]}{1} \times \frac{100}{1}$$

$$= \left[\frac{21}{20} \times \frac{25}{26} \times \frac{25}{26} - 1\right] \times \frac{100}{1}$$

$$= \left[\frac{21 \times 5 \times 25}{4 \times 26 \times 26} - 1\right] \times \frac{100}{1}$$

$$= \left[\frac{2625}{2704} - \frac{2704}{2704}\right] \times \frac{100}{1}$$

$$= -\frac{79}{2704} \times \frac{100}{1}$$

$$= -2.9\%$$

The meaning of the negative sign can be understood from a consideration of (3.5); $(R_2 - R_1)$ will be negative if R_1 is greater than R_2. Hence the negative sign of the result implies that the resistance has decreased by 2.9%.

Ratio change

The heat generated by an electric current in a conductor is proportional to the resistance of the conductor and to the square of the current. If the resistance is doubled in value and the current is reduced in the ratio $3:2$, calculate, as a ratio, the change in the heat generated.

In general

$$\text{Heat} \propto I^2 R$$

$$\therefore \text{ Heat} = kI^2 R$$

$$\therefore H_1 = kI_1{}^2 R_1$$

$$\therefore H_2 = kI_2{}^2 R_2$$

$$\therefore \frac{H_1}{H_2} = \frac{kI_1{}^2 R_1}{kI_2{}^2 R_2}$$

$$= \left(\frac{I_1}{I_2}\right)^2 \cdot \left(\frac{R_1}{R_2}\right)$$

$$= \left(\frac{3}{2}\right)^2 \cdot \frac{1}{2}$$

$$= \frac{9}{4} \cdot \frac{1}{2}$$

$$\therefore \frac{H_1}{H_2} = \frac{9}{8}$$

Therefore the heat generated has been reduced in the ratio $9:8$.

In each of these two examples, the student should note that the constant of proportionality is eliminated and that the use of suffixes with the variables is of great assistance in this type of calculation.

3.2   Square law

Example 3.5.   Area of a circle $= \pi r^2$.

We recognize π as the constant of proportionality introduced into a more general statement that the area of a circle is directly proportional to the square of the radius. This means that if the radius of a circle is doubled, then the area is multiplied by 2^2, i.e., four times; if the radius is multiplied by 3, then the area increases by 3^2, i.e., nine times. The area grows at a much faster rate than the radius, which is easily recognized if the graph of area and radius is drawn. (See Fig. 3.7.)

For equal increase in radius, PQ, QR, and RS, the corresponding increases in area, AB, CD, and EF are becoming rapidly larger. If in the function $A = \pi r^2$, r^2 is replaced by X, so that $A = \pi X$, we could regard this relation as one involving first powers only of the two variables; the

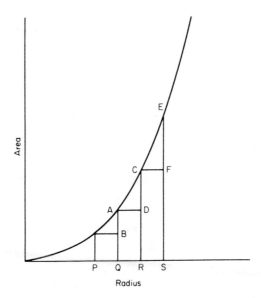

Fig. 3.7

graph of A and X would then be a straight line whose gradient A/X would give a measure of π.

r	1	2	3	4	5	6
A	3·14	12·6	28·3	50·3	78·5	112
$X = r^2$	1	4	9	16	25	36

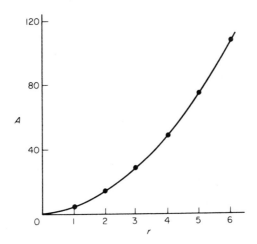

Fig. 3.8

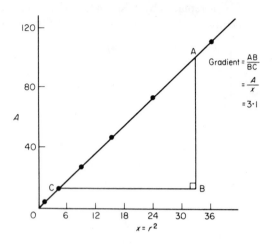

Fig. 3.9

Example 3.6. The following observations record the force F between two magnetic poles, distance d apart. Investigate the dependence of F on d.

d	1	2	3	4	5	6
F	18	4·5	2	1·1	0·72	0·5

It is clearly noticeable that as d increases, F decreases; if d is doubled in value, say from 2 to 4, then F decreases by much more than half. This suggests that F is inversely proportional to a function of d, and that the power of d is higher than unity.

Suppose $F \propto 1/d^2$, then $F = k(1/d^2)$.

Let $X = 1/d^2$, then $F = kX$.

If the graph of F and X now produces a straight line, then our supposition, $F \propto 1/d^2$, is correct.

d	1	2	3	4	5	6
F	18	4·5	2	1·1	0·72	0·5
d^2	1	4	9	16	25	36
$X = 1/d^2$	1	0·25	0·11	0·063	0·04	0·028

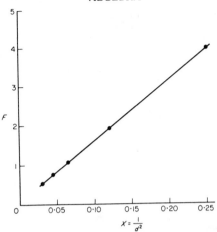

$$X = \frac{1}{d^2}$$

Fig. 3.10

The graph confirms that the force between two magnetic poles is inversely proportional to the square of their distance apart.

Example 3.7. Boyle's law, connecting the pressure and volume of a gas, states that $PV = k$, a constant.

$$P = k \times \frac{1}{V}$$

Hence pressure is inversely proportional to volume, temperature remaining constant.

Example 3.8. Joule's Laws of heating.
If an electric current flows in a conductor, the heat developed is directly and jointly proportional to the time t for which the current flows, the resistance of the conductor and to the square of the current. Hence,

$$\text{Heat} \propto I^2 Rt$$
$$\text{Heat} = kI^2 Rt \text{ J}$$

If I is measured in amperes, R in ohms, and t in seconds, and the constant k unity, then the units of heat are Joules.

Example 3.9. Simple pendulum.
The time T of one complete swing of a simple pendulum is given by,

$$T = 2\pi \sqrt{\frac{l}{g}}$$

where l is the length and g the gravitational constant. Hence T is directly proportional to the square root of the length, i.e., $T \propto \sqrt{l}$, the constant of proportionality then being $2\pi/\sqrt{g}$.

Example 3.10. The intensity of the magnetic field of a short bar magnet at a distance which is large compared with the length of the magnet, is inversely proportional to the cube of the distance. If the intensity is 10 units at a distance of 30 cm, find the intensity at a distance of 20 cm.

Let H represent the intensity of the field.

$$\therefore\ H \propto \frac{1}{d^3}$$

$$\therefore\ H = k \times \frac{1}{d^3}$$

$$= k \times \frac{1}{30^3}$$

$$\therefore\ 10 = k \times \frac{1}{30^3}$$

$$\therefore\ k = 10 \times 30^3$$

$$\therefore\ H = 10 \times 30^3 \times \frac{1}{d^3}$$

At $d = 20$,
$$H = 10 \times 30^3 \times \frac{1}{20^3}$$

$$= \frac{10 \times 27}{8}$$

$$= 33 \cdot 75 \text{ units}$$

EXERCISE 3.1

1. The weight of bronze telephone wire for a given length varies as the square of the diameter. If the weight of 1 km of wire of diameter 2 mm is 19·4 kg, find an expression for the weight W, in terms of the diameter d, and plot a graph of W against d for values of d up to 4 mm. From your graph find the weight of 1 km of wire of diameter 1·13 mm and the diameter of wire which weighs 45·5 kg per kilometre.

E.M.E.U.

2. The power developed by a motor boat engine is roughly proportional to the square of the boat's speed. Tests on a boat gave the following values:

Speed V (m/s)	2	4	6	8	10	12
Power P ($W \times 10^{-3}$)	0·6	2·5	5·4	9·3	14·5	20·8

Copy the table and add a third row of figures showing values of V^2 and plot P against V^2. Hence show that the relationship stated above is reasonably correct over this range of speed, and find a probable value for the constant k in the formula $P = kV^2$.

N.C.T.E.C.

3. The force F between two magnetic poles varies directly as the strengths m_1 and m_2 and inversely as the square of the distance apart, d. Write down the formula with a constant k connecting F, m_1, m_2, and d. If $F = 4$ when $m_1 = 3$, $m_2 = 7$, and $d = 2·5$, find F when $m_1 = 4$, $m_2 = 9$, and $d = 3·5$.

C.G.L.I. T.T. (part Qn.)

4. The results in the table below show how the length (x cm) of a given piece of wire varies when subjected to a load (W g). Show by drawing a suitable graph that the law $W = ax + b$ is approximately true and establish from your graph, values for the constants a and b.

x (cm)	12·51	13·11	13·50	14·13	14·52	14·85
W (g)	80	136	172	215	256	285

C.G.L.I. T.T. (part Qn.)

5. The resistance (R) of a wire varies directly as the length (l) of the wire and inversely as the square of the diameter (d).
   (a) Write down a formula connecting R, l and d.
   (b) If $R = 3·75\ \Omega$ for a wire 150 cm long having a diameter 0·015 cm, find the constant of variation and express it in standard form.
   (c) Calculate the length of wire of diameter 0·01 cm which has a resistance of 10 Ω.

C.G.L.I. E.T. (part Qn.)

6. (a) The voltage drop V in a conductor varies directly as the length l of the conductor and inversely as the square of its diameter d. If l is increased by 50%, and d increased by 25%, find the resulting percentage change in V. State whether V increases or decreases.
   (b) The wavelength λ of a radio wave is inversely proportional to its frequency f. If a wavelength of 60 m corresponds to a frequency of 5 MHz, determine a formula giving λ in terms of f, and plot a graph to show the relationship between λ and f for

the range $f = 1$ MHz to $f = 10$ MHz. From the graph determine,

(i) the value of λ when $f = 7.6$ MHz,

(ii) the value of f when $\lambda = 125$ m.

C.G.L.I. E.T.

7. The field strength E at a distance D from a radio transmitter varies directly as the height H of the receiving aerial and as the square root of the radiated power P and inversely as the square of the distance D.

(a) If $E = 18\ \mu A/m$ when $P = 2000$ W, $H = 30$ m, and $D = 8$ km, derive an expression for E in terms of P, H, and D, evaluating the constant factor involved.

(b) Hence calculate the field strength at an aerial 40 m high located 10 km from the same transmitter.

C.G.L.I. E.T.

8. The heating effect H of an electric current varies as the square of the voltage V and inversely as resistance R. If V is halved and R is trebled, by what ratio is H changed?

U.E.I. (part Qn.)

9. The resistance R of a conductor is directly proportional to its length l and inversely proportional to the square of its diameter d. For a conductor 100 m long of diameter 10^{-3} m, the resistance is 20,000 ohms. Calculate the constant of proportionality. If both the length and diameter of the above conductor were to be increased by 10%, calculate the new resistance.

U.L.C.I.

10. (a) The resistance R of a wire is directly proportional to its length l and inversely proportional to the square of the diameter d. If l is trebled and d is doubled, by what ratio is R changed?

(b) The energy due to an electric current is proportional to the square of the applied voltage. If a heater is designed to work at x V, but the voltage rises by y V, find in its simplest form, the percentage increase in energy.

Y.C.

11. The illumination E on a surface, due to a point source of light, for varying distances d, between source and surface, is given by the following table:

E	70	40	25	18	13
d	3	4	5	6	7

(a) Plot E(y-axis) against $1/d^2$(x-axis),

(b) Determine, with the aid of the graph, the law connecting E and d.

Y.C.

12. The amount of heat produced by an electric current is proportional to the square of the current, the resistance of the conductor and the time for which the current flows. A current of 1·5 A flowing through a wire of resistance 12·25 Ω for 10 minutes produces 16·6 kJ. Find the amount of heat produced by a current of 3A flowing through a wire of resistance 6·5 Ω for 1 minute.

Y.C. (part Qn.)

13. The electrical resistance of a copper wire of circular cross-section varies directly as its length and inversely as the square of its diameter. If two copper wires have the same resistance, but the diameter of one is twice that of the other, obtain the ratio of their lengths. Hence show that the thicker wire is sixteen times as heavy as the thinner wire.

Y.C. (part Qn.)

14. The weight of a sphere is proportional to the specific gravity of the material and the cube of its diameter. Express this in the form of an equation.

A sphere of diameter 8 cm, made of a metal of specific gravity 3·56, weighs 32 g. Calculate the weight of a sphere of specific gravity 5·34 and diameter 6 cm.

U.E.I.

15. The magnetic reluctance S of an iron bar of length l and diameter d is directly proportional to the length and inversely proportional to the square of the diameter. If the reluctance is 25×10^{-6} units when $l = 0.25$ and $d = 4$, calculate the value of the constant of proportionality. If l is doubled and d is halved, calculate the new value of the reluctance.

U.L.C.I.

16. The force F on a current-carrying conductor in a magnetic field is directly proportional to I, the current flowing in the conductor, the intensity of the magnetic field H, and the length of the conductor l. If $F = 75$ when $I = 5$, $H = 1.5$, and $l = 100$, find the constant of proportionality.

17. The volume of a cone is directly proportional to its height and the square of its radius. If the height of a cone increases by 8%, and its radius decreases by 4%, calculate the percentage change in volume.

18. The magnetizing force in a certain solenoid is directly proportional to the current flowing, and the number of turns of wire and inversely proportional to the length of the core. If the current is increased in the ratio 3:5, and the number of turns increased in the ratio 4:5, while the length of core is increased in the ratio 3:4, calculate the ratio by which the magnetizing force has changed.

19. The mutual inductance between two coils is directly proportional to the square root of the product of the two self-inductances. If the self-inductance of one coil increases by 25% and the other decreases by 4%, calculate the percentage change in the mutual inductance.

20. The magnetic field strength due to a long straight current-carrying conductor is directly proportional to the current flowing and inversely proportional to the distance from the conductor. If the current is increased by 10% and the distance by 5%, calculate the percentage change in field strength.

3.3   Determination of laws; straight-line graphs

In chapter 8 of Vol. 1, it was shown that a straight-line graph resulted from a relation of two variables which did not involve any higher power than unity. In this form, we were able to measure two properties of the graphs which represented two constants in the functional relationship, namely gradient and intercept.

Consider the length of a wire or spring, stretched by a given load

$$l = aW + b$$

In terms of proportion or variation, this could be expressed as follows: the length is the sum of two parts, one of which is constant and the other directly proportional to the load applied.

The constant part, represented by b, is the unstretched natural length of the wire with no load applied. The other part, represented by aW, is the extension caused by the load W, 'a' therefore being the constant of proportionality. This will be more readily understood if we consider two loads W_1 and W_2 producing lengths l_1 and l_2.

$$l_2 = aW_2 + b$$
$$l_1 = aW_1 + b$$

Subtracting, $$l_2 - l_1 = aW_2 - aW_1$$
$$\therefore\ l_2 - l_1 = a(W_2 - W_1)$$

Hence the extension $(l_2 - l_1) \propto$ extra load $(W_2 - W_1)$. The functions studied in Vol. 1 then, are examples of part variation.

In §3.2 above, using $A = \pi r^2$, the graph produced by plotting variables A and r was a parabola, from which it was not possible to identify the constant π. If X replaced r^2, the graph of A and X was a straight line whose gradient represented the constant of proportionality, π.

The purpose of our present study is to consider the two effects just referred to, part variation and variables whose power is greater or less than unity. Our aim is to modify the given function so that it takes the linear form, $y = mx + c$.

Example 3.11. The following values of x and y were observed and are thought to follow a law of the form, $y = ax + bx^2$. By drawing a suitable graph, test if this is so and find approximate values of a and b.

x	1	2	3	4	5
y	2	5·6	10·8	17·6	26

$$y = ax + bx^2$$

Divide through by x,

$$\therefore \frac{y}{x} = a + bx$$

which is now in linear form on the r.h.s. For the l.h.s., let $Y = y/x$,

$$\therefore Y = a + bx$$

If, now, we add another line of values, representing y/x, to the given table of values, and draw the graph of Y and x, the resulting straight line will show gradient b and intercept a.

x	1	2	3	4	5
y	2	5·6	10·8	17·6	26
$Y = y/x$	2	2·8	3·6	4·4	5·2

It is supposed that the given values are the result of experiment, and as such will contain errors. The choice of 'best straight line' to fit the points plotted will average out these errors. The values of a and b must, therefore, be measured or calculated from the graph and not from the table of observations.

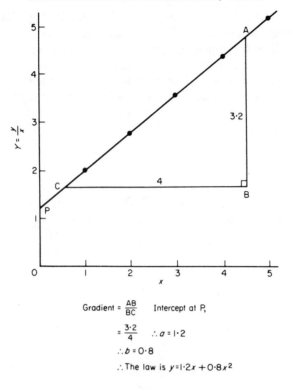

Gradient $= \dfrac{AB}{BC}$ Intercept at P,

$\qquad = \dfrac{3 \cdot 2}{4} \qquad \therefore a = 1 \cdot 2$

$\therefore b = 0 \cdot 8$

$\therefore$ The law is $y = 1 \cdot 2x + 0 \cdot 8x^2$

Fig. 3.11

Example 3.12. The value of a quantity R is the sum of two parts, one of which is constant, and the other is inversely proportional to the square of d. Write down an expression showing the connection between R and d, and by drawing a suitable graph, determine whether the following observations satisfy this relation. From your graph, evaluate the constants of the expression.

d	0·1	0·3	0·5	0·7	0·9	1·0
R	50	183	194	197	198	198·5

Let $R = A + B$, let $A = k$, a constant, and let $B \propto 1/d^2$. Therefore

$$B = c\,\frac{1}{d^2}$$

and $$R = k + \frac{c}{d^2}$$

Let $D = 1/d^2$,

$$\therefore\ R = k + cD$$

Plot R against D, showing gradient c and intercept k from the straight-line graph.

d	0·1	0·3	0·5	0·7	0·9	1·0
R	50	183	194	197	198	198·5
$D = 1/d^2$	100	11·1	4	2	1·2	1·0

If the first point, $R = 50$, $D = 100$, is omitted from the graph, the improvement in scale on the horizontal axis will lead to greater accuracy.

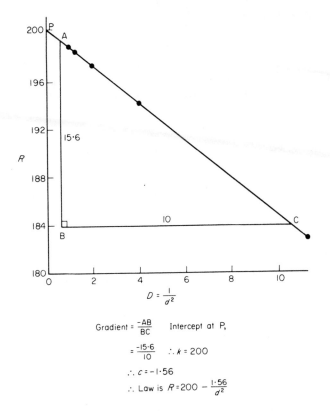

Gradient $= \dfrac{-AB}{BC}$ Intercept at P,

$= \dfrac{-15·6}{10}$ $\therefore k = 200$

$\therefore c = -1·56$

$\therefore$ Law is $R = 200 - \dfrac{1·56}{d^2}$

Fig. 3.12

The negative sign attached to AB indicates that R decreases in value as D increases in value from B to C.

Example 3.13. Type $y = ax^n$ Plotting of logarithmic values.
If the relation between two variables, x and y, is of the form, $y = ax^n$,

the modification required to obtain a straight-line graph is achieved by writing the function in logarithmic form

$$y = ax^n$$
$$\therefore \log_{10} y = \log_{10} (ax^n)$$
$$= \log_{10} a + \log_{10} x^n$$
$$= \log_{10} a + n \log_{10} x$$
$$= n \log_{10} x + \log_{10} a$$

which is now in the form,

$$y = mx + c$$

Hence we plot $\log_{10} y$ and $\log_{10} x$, the gradient being represented by n and the intercept by $\log_{10} a$; from this we shall obtain a by finding the antilogarithm.

Example 3.14. The pressure and volume of a gas follow a law of the form, $pv^n = C$. Draw a suitable straight-line graph to show that the following observations satisfy this law and from the graph find approximate values of n and C.

v	1·33	2·37	4·22	7·94	13·3	20·0
p	398	200	80·4	44·7	20·0	12·6

$$pv^n = C$$
$$\therefore p = \frac{C}{v^n} = Cv^{-n}$$
$$\therefore \log_{10} p = \log_{10} C + \log_{10} (v^{-n})$$
$$= \log_{10} C - n \log_{10} v$$

This is now in straight-line form if we regard $\log_{10} p$ as the y co-ordinate and $\log_{10} v$ as the x co-ordinate. The gradient is represented by n and the intercept by $\log_{10} C$.

$\log_{10} v$	0·124	0·375	0·625	0·900	1·12	1·30
$\log_{10} p$	2·60	2·30	1·91	1·65	1·30	1·10

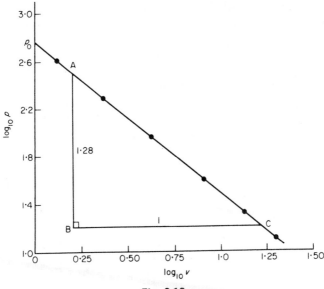

Fig. 3.13

Gradient

Draw a large right-angled triangle ABC, using part of the straight line as hypotenuse; choose the length of BC to be a convenient number of units, measured on the log v axis. Measure the length of AB in the units of the log p axis.

$$\text{Gradient} = -\frac{AB}{BC} = -\frac{1\cdot28}{1} = -1\cdot28$$

Intercept

Since the log v axis is graduated from zero, then the intercept can be read on the log p axis at p_0.

$$\log_{10} C = 2\cdot76$$
$$\therefore\ C = 575$$

Conclusion

The observations, plotted in logarithmic values, produce a straight-line graph, and therefore satisfy a law of the form,

$$\log_{10} p = \log_{10} C - n \log_{10} v$$
$$\therefore\ pv^{1\cdot28} = 575$$

Logarithmic graph paper

When the variables of a graph are to be plotted in logarithmic values, it is convenient to use graph paper printed for this purpose. The graduations have properties similar to those on a slide rule, i.e., the lengths are logarithmic values, but the numerical graduations are real numbers. The same concentration of scale occurs towards the higher values of the numbers 1 to 10.

Logarithmic graph paper is classified in 'cycles', which is an indication of the range of values for which it can be used. A cycle in this respect means an integral power of 10. Thus log 3 cycles × 2 cycles means that along the y-axis, or vertical axis, we can plot a range of values extending over 3 integral powers of 10, and over 2 integral powers of 10 along the x-axis or horizontal axis.

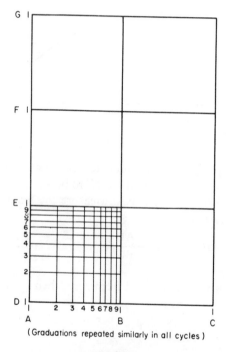

(Graduations repeated similarly in all cycles)

Fig. 3.14

The letters A to C and D to G are not printed on logarithmic paper and are shown in Fig. 3.14 to guide the reader in this discussion. There are 3 cycles on the vertical axis, D to E, E to F, and F to G, and 2 cycles on the horizontal axis, A to B and B to C. At each of these lettered points, the figure 1 represents an integral power of 10, the powers at D and A being chosen in accordance with the range of values to be plotted. If D is 10^1, then E, F, and G are 10^2, 10^3, and 10^4 respectively, thus allowing a range of values from 10 to 10,000.

If D is 10^{-2}, then E, F, and G are 10^{-1}, 10^0, and 10^1 respectively, giving a range from 0·01 to 10.

Example 3.15. The following values are to be plotted on logarithmic graph paper; state the classification of cycles.

x	0·5	1·2	5·8	11·3	32·7
y	0·015	0·043	0·079	0·082	0·097

The values of x lie between 0·1 and 100, i.e., between 10^{-1} and 10^2, thus occurring in the 3 cycles, 10^{-1} to 10^0, 10^0 to 10^1, and 10^1 to 10^2. The values of y lie between 0·01 and 0·1, i.e., between 10^{-2} and 10^{-1}, which is 1 cycle. The correct style of paper to be used would be classified as log 1 cycle × 3 cycles.

It is important to note that logarithmic paper must be used as printed: it cannot be 'turned round' in order to obtain a longer axis in a particular direction.

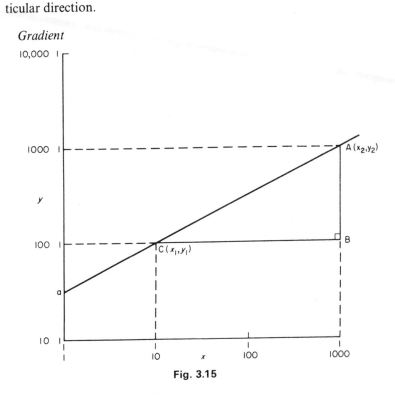

Fig. 3.15

Since numbers only are printed on logarithmic paper, the axes are denoted by x and y, not log x and log y.

Consider $$y = ax^n$$

$$\log y = n \log x + \log a$$

The gradient n is the ratio $\log y / \log x$, represented in Fig. 3.15 by AB/BC, i.e.,

$$\frac{\log y_2 - \log y_1}{\log x_2 - \log x_1}$$

This ratio will be the same as the ratio of the lengths of AB and BC measured in inches or centimetres. In Fig. 3.15, the lengths of AB and BC are in the ratio $1:2$, giving a gradient of $\frac{1}{2}$. This is confirmed if we use,

$$n = \frac{\log y_2 - \log y_1}{\log x_2 - \log x_1}$$

$$= \frac{\log 1000 - \log 100}{\log 1000 - \log 10}$$

$$= \frac{3 - 2}{3 - 1} = \frac{1}{2}$$

Hence $$\text{Gradient} = \frac{\text{measured length of AB}}{\text{measured length of BC}}$$

Intercept

The intercept can be read directly at 'a' if the x-axis is graduated from zero; this will be true in Fig. 3.15, since $x = 1$ gives $\log x = 0$.

Example 3.16. Show by a graphical method that the following observations of H and n are connected by a law of the form, $H = cn^k$, and find approximate values of c and k.

n	1·33	2·24	3·55	5·62	8·41	15·9
H	21·9	28·8	38·0	50·1	63·1	91·2

$$H = cn^k$$

$$\therefore \log_{10} H = \log c + k \log n$$

$$\therefore \log H = k \log n + \log c$$

We shall plot $\log H$ on the vertical axis and $\log n$ on the horizontal axis. The gradient is represented by k and the intercept by $\log c$.

Since the values of n lie between 1 and 100, i.e., between 10^0 and 10^2, we shall require 2 cycles along the x-axis, using logarithmic paper. The values of H lie between 10 and 100, i.e., between 10^1 and 10^2, thus requiring 1 cycle. The style of paper is therefore, log 1 cycle × 2 cycles.

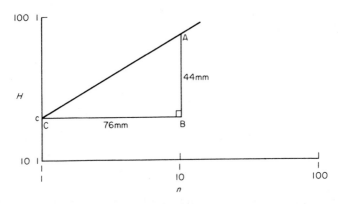

Fig. 3.16

$$\text{Gradient} = k = \frac{AB}{BC} = \frac{44}{76}$$

$$k = 0.58$$

Intercept. Read directly on H-axis at c,

$$c = 18.4$$

Hence the observations satisfy the law,

$$H = 18.4n^{0.58}$$

EXERCISE 3.2

Modify the variables of the following functions to show a linear relationship; state the co-ordinates to be plotted and the constants which represent the gradient and intercept on the graph.

1. $y = ax^2 + b$

2. $y = m\sqrt{x} + c$

3. $E = k + \dfrac{c}{I}$ variables E and I

4. $s = ut + \frac{1}{2}ft^2$ variables s and t

5. $Z^2 = K + X^2$ variables Z and X

6. $y = \dfrac{a}{x} + bx$

7. $y = \dfrac{a}{b - x}$

8. $y = \dfrac{1}{ax + b}$

9. $y = \dfrac{a}{b + x^2}$

10. $y = a\sqrt{x} + \dfrac{b}{\sqrt{x}}$

11. By plotting a suitable graph, verify that a formula of the type $v = a + bi^2$ holds for the following data:

i	1·60	2·35	2·74	3·37	3·89
v	20	32	40	56	70

From your graph, obtain values for the constants a and b.

C.G.L.I. T.T.

12. The current i in a certain circuit is believed to vary with the voltage v according to the law $v = a + bi^n$, where n may have the value 1 or 2. Observation gave the following results:

v	15	25	35	50	70
i	1·12	1·95	2·50	3·16	3·89

Which is the more likely index for i? Using this index, find the values of a and b.

C.G.L.I.

13. The following values are velocities (V) and the corresponding resistances (R) due to friction, of a certain machine.

Velocity (V)	15	20	25	30	35
Resistance (R)	5·4	10·2	17·0	25·2	35·0

The law connecting these quantities is thought to be of the form $R = aV + bV^2$ where a and b are constants. By plotting the appropriate straight-line graph, verify the law and determine the probable values of a and b.

N.C.T.E.C.

14. The number of teeth (T) to put in a milling cutter having a diameter (D) is given by $T = k\sqrt{D} - c$. From the following series of measurements, plot a suitable graph to obtain values of k and c.

D	2	3	4	5	6	7
T	14	18	22	25	28	31

15. The current i mA through a rectifier in the conducting direction is shown below, measured for values of the applied voltage v volts.

v	8	12	18	25	32
i	3·4	5·9	10·5	17·9	26·8

Assuming an approximate formula, $i = av + bv^2$ holds, plot suitable variables to obtain a straight-line graph, and thence obtain estimates for the constants a and b.

C.G.L.I. T.T.

16. The following results were obtained in measuring the inductance L of a coil of t turns;

t	4	5	6	7	8	9
L	$15\frac{1}{2}$	21	$27\frac{1}{2}$	$35\frac{1}{2}$	$44\frac{1}{2}$	$54\frac{1}{2}$

By plotting L against t^2 show that these results satisfy a law of the form $L = at^2 + b$. From your graph, find suitable values of a and b.

E.M.E.U.

17. The frictional losses P in a machine are the sum of two quantities, one directly proportional to the speed N, and the other directly proportional to N^2. Write down an expression connecting P and N, and by plotting a suitable straight-line graph, verify that the following observations satisfy the expression. From your graph find the constants of proportionality.

N	620	740	880	1100	1250	1500
P	138	184	242	353	431	600

18. The breakdown voltage of an insulating material is given approximately by the law,

$$V = at^{2/3}$$

Plot a suitable straight-line graph to verify that the following observations on samples of mica satisfy the law. From your graph, find an approximate value of a.

t (mm)	0·05	0·06	0·08	0·10	0·15	0·20	0·25
V (kV)	13·6	15·5	18·6	21·5	28·2	34·3	39·7

19. For a cable supplying current, the total financial loss per annum, £P, is given by $P = ka + c/a$ where a is the cross-sectional area. The first term, ka, represents interest and depreciation, the term c/a represents power losses due to the resistance of the cable. Verify graphically that the following values satisfy this law and find approximate values for k and c.

a	1	1·5	2·0	2·5	3·0	3·5
P	120	96	90	90	93	98

20. The following measurements of the luminosity (I) of an electric lamp with varying voltage (V) were obtained:

V	60	80	100	120	140	160
I	6·5	20·5	50	104	192	328

By drawing a graph of log I against log V, show that a law of the form $I = aV^n$ is followed. Hence find suitable values of n and a, giving the result for a in standard form.

E.M.E.U.

21. A certain experiment gave the following pairs of observed values of two related variables q and v:

q	2	5	10	15	25
v	22	49	72	83	101

Plot v against $\log_{10} q$ and hence show that the relationship is of the form $v = k \log_{10} q$. Find the value of the constant k as accurately as possible. The relationship can alternatively be written in the form, $q = a^v$, where a is a constant. Find the value of a corresponding to your value of k.

N.C.T.E.C.

22. The luminance B cd/m^2 of the trace on a cathode-ray tube varies with the applied voltage E as shown below:

E	50	60	70	80
B	40	65	96	136

Assuming the luminance to vary as a power of the voltage, obtain with the aid of a graph an approximate formula giving B in terms of E.

C.G.L.I. T.T.

23. The following values of current i and voltage v were observed in a certain circuit and are thought to follow a law of the form, $i = kv^n$. Draw a suitable graph to test this and from it find approximate values of the constants k and n.

i	1·0	2·5	8·7	18·1	30·3	45·5
v	0·6	1·0	2·0	3·0	4·0	5·0

24. The values of two variables Q and H are recorded below. Test whether these values satisfy a law of the form $H = aQ^n$ and find approximate values of the constants a and n.

Q	10	15	20	25	30	35
H	0·044	0·027	0·019	0·015	0·012	0·010

25. The pressure and volume of a gas are related by a law of the form, $pv^n = C$. Determine whether the following observations satisfy this law and find values of n and C.

p	156	120	97·3	80·9	68·7	59·0
v	2·5	3·0	3·5	4·0	4·5	5·0

3.4 Transformation of formulae

Continued practice in the use of formulae in evaluation and transposition requires only the methods described in chapter 2 of Vol. 1. As briefly as possible, these are repeated here. Our aim is always to break the existing mathematical links between the terms of the formula in order to isolate one particular term. The general order of operations is found to be as follows:

(a) clear square root operations if present,
(b) clear fractions,
(c) multiply brackets,
(d) collect terms,
(e) choose a common factor,
(f) divide by the other factor.

Example 3.17. The time period of a certain compound pendulum was given by,

$$T = 4\pi \sqrt{\left\{\frac{(M + 2m)l}{2(M + 3m)g}\right\}}$$

Transpose this formula to make m the subject.

$$T = 4\pi \sqrt{\left\{\frac{(M + 2m)l}{2(M + 3m)g}\right\}}$$

Square both sides:

$$T^2 = 16\pi^2 \frac{(M + 2m)l}{2(M + 3m)g}$$

Multiply both sides by $2(M + 3m)g$:

$$2(M + 3m)gT^2 = 16\pi^2(M + 2m)l$$

Multiply brackets:

$$2gT^2 M + 2gT^2 3m = 16\pi^2 Ml + 32\pi^2 ml$$

Collect terms containing m:

$$2gT^2 3m - 32\pi^2 lm = 16\pi^2 Ml - 2gT^2 M$$

Write m as a common factor:

$$m(6gT^2 - 32\pi^2 l) = 16\pi^2 Ml - 2gT^2 M$$

Divide by the other factor:

$$m = \frac{16\pi^2 Ml - 2gT^2 M}{(6gT^2 - 32\pi^2 l)}$$

$$= \frac{2M(8\pi^2 l - gT^2)}{2(3gT^2 - 16\pi^2 l)}$$

$$= \frac{M(8\pi^2 l - gT^2)}{(3gT^2 - 16\pi^2 l)}$$

If students will define in words the process they choose to operate many of their difficulties will disappear. It may be appropriate to summarize the few processes involved at this stage.

(a) multiply, divide, add or subtract,
(b) raise to a power, e.g., square or cube,
(c) find a square root or cube root, basically the same as (b),
(d) factorize,
(e) apply a common denominator.

It is important to recognize that the process of 'taking a term from one side of a formula to the other' does not feature in this list and indeed does not exist. One cannot see into the parcel without dealing with the wrappings first.

EXERCISE 3.3

1. Transpose the formula,

$$\frac{E - e}{R - x} = e\left(\frac{1}{x} + \frac{1}{r}\right)$$

to give e in terms of the other quantities, and hence find the value of e, given that $R = 5$, $x = 3$, $E = 2$, and $r = 2$.

E.M.E.U.

2. If

$$f = \frac{1}{2\pi\sqrt{LC}}$$

find a formula expressing L in terms of f and C. Find L if $C = 0.4 \times 10^{-6}$ and $f = 24 \times 10^3$.

U.E.I. (part Qn.)

3. The oscillating frequency of the discharge of a condenser is given by,

$$\omega = \sqrt{\left(\frac{1}{LC} - \frac{R^2}{4L^2}\right)}$$

Transpose the formula to give C in terms of the other quantities.

E.M.E.U. (part Qn.)

4. If the resonant frequency f_r for a parallel circuit is given by the formula,

$$f_r = \frac{1}{2\pi}\sqrt{\left(\frac{1}{LC} - \frac{R^2}{L^2}\right)}$$

transpose the formula to obtain C in terms of the other quantities. If $f_r = 52$, $L = 50 \times 10^{-3}$, and $R = 20$, calculate the value of C.

E.M.E.U. (part Qn.)

5. Rearrange the following formula which occurs in the theory of frequency modulation, to make L_1 the subject.

$$f = \frac{1}{2\pi} \sqrt{\left(\frac{L_1 + L_2}{L_1 L_2}\right)}$$

Write down the formula for L_2.

C.G.L.I. T.T. (part Qn.)

6. If

$$Z = \sqrt{\{R^2 + (X_1 - X_2)^2\}}$$

rearrange the formula to obtain an expression for X_2.

C.G.L.I. E.T. (part Qn.)

7. The impedance Z ohms of a series circuit containing resistance R ohms, inductance L henrys, and capacitance C farads, is given by

$$Z = \sqrt{\left\{R^2 + \left(\omega L - \frac{1}{\omega C}\right)^2\right\}}$$

(a) Calculate Z when $R = 15$, $L = 0{\cdot}02$, $\omega = 2100$, and $C = 8 \times 10^{-6}$.

(b) If $\omega = 2\pi f$, where f is frequency in Hz, determine the frequency at which $Z = R$.

C.G.L.I. E.T. (part Qn.)

8. If

$$\omega = \sqrt{\left(\frac{1}{LC} - \frac{R^2}{4L^2}\right)}$$

find an expression for R.

C.G.L.I. E.T. (part Qn.)

9. If

$$h = \frac{2k}{\sqrt{(b^2 - 3a)}}$$

express b in terms of h, k, and a and find the value of b when $h = 2$, $k = 3$, and $a = -1$.

N.C.T.E.C. (part Qn.)

10. The current in a circuit containing resistance, inductance, and capacitance in series is given by,

$$I = \frac{V}{\sqrt{\left\{R^2 + \left(\omega L - \frac{1}{\omega C}\right)^2\right\}}}$$

Transpose this formula to make L the subject.

11. If

$$R = R_2 + \frac{R_1 R_2}{R_1 + R_2}$$

find a formula for R_1 in terms of R and R_2.

12. A formula used in connection with a triode valve is,

$$G = \frac{\mu R}{r + (\mu + 1)R}$$

Make μ the subject of the formula.

4. Geometry

4.1 Properties of the circle

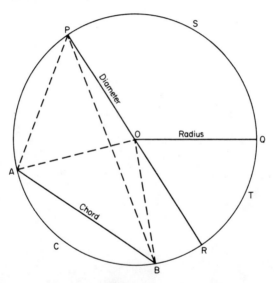

Fig. 4.1

The radius and diameter of a circle have been introduced in chapter 6 of Vol. 1. The following additional definitions will enable us to study a wider range of circle properties.

Chord

A chord of a circle is any straight line whose ends lie on the circumference of the circle, e.g., AB in Fig. 4.1.

Arc

An arc is any part of the circumference, e.g., ACB or APQRB in Fig. 4.1.

Segment

A segment of a circle is an area between a chord and an arc, e.g., the area between AB and ACB; this is known as a minor segment, being less than half the area of the circle. The area between AB and APQRB is a major segment.

Sector

A sector of a circle is an area whose boundaries are two radii and an arc, e.g., OPSQ and OQTR in Fig. 4.1.

Tangent

A tangent to a circle is any straight line drawn outside the circle which has only one point of contact with the circumference of the circle, e.g., XY and LM in Fig. 4.2. A tangent is said to touch a circle.

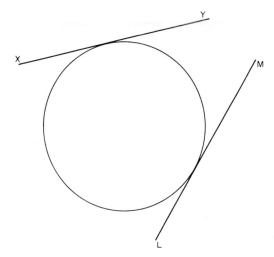

Fig. 4.2

'Subtends'

This word is used mainly in connection with angles in a circle. Referring to Fig. 4.1, we say that the chord AB subtends the angle AOB at the centre of the circle or the arc QR subtends the angle QOR at the centre. The chord AB also subtends the angle APB at the circumference of the circle. An alternative meaning for 'subtends' could be 'stands on';

thus angle APB stands on chord AB or on arc ACB. In general, the angle properties of a circle are restricted to the two positions, centre and circumference.

4.2   Theorems

Theorems are generalized statements of particular properties which apply to all figures of the same type, whatever their size; they can be proved to be true without reference to particular dimensions.

We are not concerned in this book with proofs, but accept their results as aids to calculations.

(a)

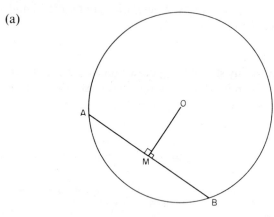

Fig. 4.3

A line, OM drawn from the centre O of a circle, at right-angles to a chord AB, will bisect the chord: hence AM = MB.

Example 4.1. Calculate the length of a chord in a circle of radius 13 cm, whose distance from the centre is 5 cm.

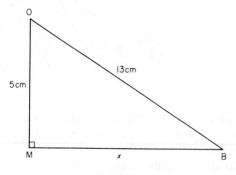

Fig. 4.4

From Fig. 4.3, we use $\triangle$OMB as in Fig. 4.4. By Pythagoras' theorem,

$$x^2 = 13^2 - 5^2$$
$$\therefore\ x^2 = 169 - 25$$
$$= 144$$
$$\therefore\ x = 12\text{ cm}$$

The chord AB is therefore 24 cm in length.

(b)

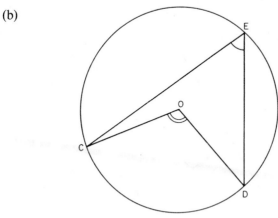

Fig. 4.5

An angle at the centre of a circle is twice the size of an angle at the circumference subtended by the same arc.

Hence, $\angle$COD $= 2 \times \angle$CED

(c)

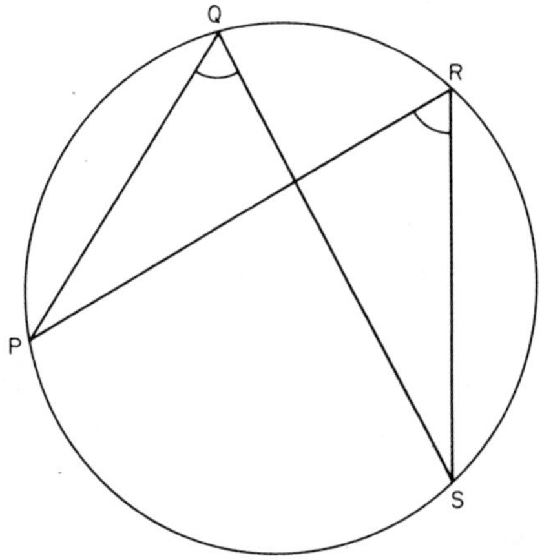

Fig. 4.6

Angles at the circumference of a circle, subtended by the same arc, are equal.

Hence, $$\angle PQS = \angle PRS$$

or $$\angle QPR = \angle QSR$$

Example 4.2. Calculate the value of angle θ in Fig. 4.7, given $\angle OAB = 40°$, $\angle BDC = 60°$, and $DA = DC$.

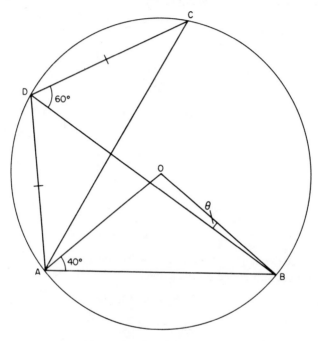

Fig. 4.7

In $\triangle OAB$, $OA = OB$ radii

$$\therefore \angle OBA = \angle OAB = 40°$$

$$\therefore \angle AOB = 180° - (40° + 40°)$$

$$= 100°$$

$$\therefore \angle ADB = 50° \qquad \text{theorem (b)}$$

and $$\angle ADC = \angle ADB + \angle BDC$$

$$= 50° + 60°$$

Therefore, in $\triangle ADC$,

$$\angle ADC = 110°$$

and $\angle DAC = \angle DCA$ since $DA = DC$

$$\therefore \ \angle DCA = \frac{180° - 110°}{2}$$

$$= 35°$$

$$\therefore \ \angle DBA = 35°$$ theorem (c)

and $\theta = \angle OBA - \angle DBA$

$$\therefore \ \theta = 40° - 35°$$

$$= 5°$$

(d) An angle at the circumference of a circle, subtended by a diameter, is a right-angle. Hence $\angle FHG = \angle FKG = 90°$.

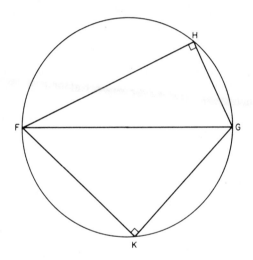

Fig. 4.8

(e) (i) The angle between a tangent and a radius to the point of contact is a right-angle. Hence $\angle OAP = \angle OBP = 90°$.

(ii) Two tangents from the same point to a circle are equal in length.

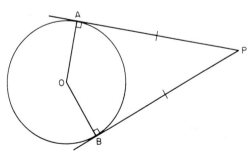

Fig. 4.9

(iii) The line PO, joining the centre of the circle to the point P from which two tangents are drawn to the circle, bisects the chord of contact, AB, at right-angles. Hence AM = MB, and all the angles at M are right-angles.

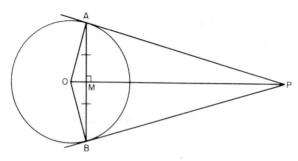

Fig. 4.10

Example 4.3. From a point, 25 cm from the centre of a circle of radius 7 cm, two tangents are drawn to the circle. Calculate the length of the chord of contact.

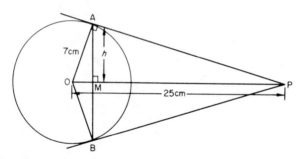

Fig. 4.11

In △OAP,

$$AP^2 = 25^2 - 7^2 = (25 + 7)(25 - 7)$$

$$\therefore AP^2 = 32 \times 18 = 64 \times 9$$

$$\therefore AP = \sqrt{64 \times 9}$$

$$\therefore AP = 8 \times 3 = 24 \text{ cm}$$

$$\text{Area } \triangle OAP = \frac{AP \times AO}{2} = \frac{24 \times 7}{2} = 84 \text{ cm}^2$$

Considering OP as the base and AM as the height of the same triangle, then

$$\text{Area } \triangle OAP = \frac{OP \times AM}{2} = \frac{25 \times h}{2}$$

$$\therefore\ 84 = \frac{25 \times h}{2}$$

$$\therefore\ h = \frac{84 \times 2}{25}$$

$$= 6.72 \text{ cm}$$

$$\therefore\ AB = 2 \times 6.72 = 13.44 \text{ cm}$$

(f) If two circles touch, externally (Fig. 4.12), or internally (Fig. 4.13), the line joining their centres passes through the point of contact.

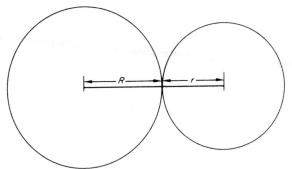

Fig. 4.12

(i) External contact. Distance between centres = $R + r$.

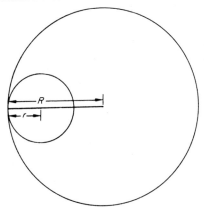

Fig. 4.13

(ii) Internal contact. Distance between centres = $R - r$.

Example 4.4. A circle is inscribed in a square of 8 cm. Calculate the radius of a circle which touches the given circle and also touches two of the sides of the square.

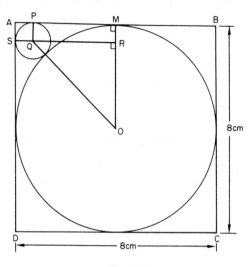

Fig. 4.14

A circle is said to be inscribed in a figure when it touches each boundary of the figure. Hence the circle centre O, touching the sides of the square ABCD, will have a radius of 4 cm. Let the required circle, centre Q, have radius r cm, making OQ $(4 + r)$ cm.

$$OM = 4 \text{ cm}, \quad \therefore \ OR = OM - MR = (4 - r) \text{ cm}$$
$$RS = 4 \text{ cm}, \quad \therefore \ RQ = RS - SQ = (4 - r) \text{ cm}$$

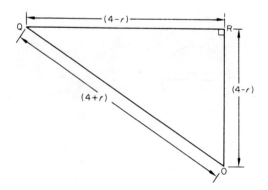

Fig. 4.15

$$\therefore \ (4 + r)^2 = (4 - r)^2 + (4 - r)^2 \qquad \text{(Pythagoras)}$$
$$\therefore \ 16 + 8r + r^2 = 16 - 8r + r^2 + 16 - 8r + r^2$$
$$\therefore \ r^2 - 24r + 16 = 0$$

Using the formula method to solve this quadratic equation,

$$\therefore \ r = \frac{24 \pm \sqrt{24^2 - 4(1)(16)}}{2}$$

$$= \frac{24 \pm \sqrt{576 - 64}}{2}$$

$$= \frac{24 \pm \sqrt{512}}{2} = \frac{24 \pm \sqrt{256 \times 2}}{2}$$

$$= \frac{24 \pm 16\sqrt{2}}{2} = 12 \pm 8\sqrt{2}$$

$$= 12 - 8 \times 1{\cdot}414$$

$$= 12 - 11{\cdot}312$$

$$= 0{\cdot}688 \text{ cm}$$

The value, $12 + 8\sqrt{2}$ is clearly impractical.

(g) If two circles intersect, the line joining their centres, OM, bisects their common chord, AB, at right-angles. Hence, in Fig. 4.16, AC = CB, and all the angles at C are right-angles.

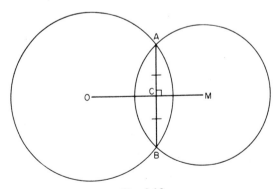

Fig. 4.16

Example 4.5. Two circles, radii 8 cm and 10 cm, have their centres 12 cm apart. Calculate the length of their common chord.

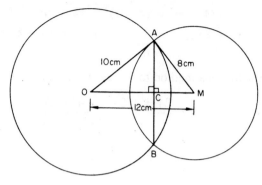

Fig. 4.17

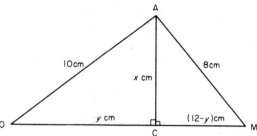

Fig. 4.18

Note that the two right-angled triangles ACO and ACM have a common side AC.

Let $AC = x$ cm and let $OC = y$ cm.

$$\therefore\ CM = (12 - y) \text{ cm}$$

In $\triangle ACO$,
$$x^2 + y^2 = 10^2$$
$$\therefore\ x^2 = 10^2 - y^2$$

$\triangle ACM$:
$$x^2 + (12 - y)^2 = 8^2$$
$$\therefore\ x^2 = 8^2 - (12 - y)^2$$
$$\therefore\ 10^2 - y^2 = 8^2 - (12 - y)^2$$
$$= 64 - (12 - y)(12 - y)$$
$$= 64 - (144 - 24y + y^2)$$
$$= 64 - 144 + 24y - y^2$$
$$\therefore\ 100 - 64 + 144 = 24y$$
$$\therefore\ 180 = 24y$$
$$\therefore\ \frac{180}{24} = y$$
$$\therefore\ y = 7\tfrac{1}{2}$$

From $x^2 = 10^2 - y^2$:

$$x^2 = 10^2 - (7\tfrac{1}{2})^2$$
$$= 100 - 56 \cdot 25$$
$$\therefore \ x = \sqrt{43 \cdot 75} = 6 \cdot 615$$
$$\therefore \ AB = 2x = 13 \cdot 2 \text{ cm}$$

(h) An angle between a chord, AT, and a tangent, TB, is equal to any angle in the alternate segment, $\angle$ACT, i.e., subtended by the chord on the opposite side to the tangent.

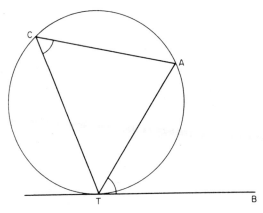

Fig. 4.19

(i) If two chords, AB and CD, intersect at E, then AE × EB = CE × ED.

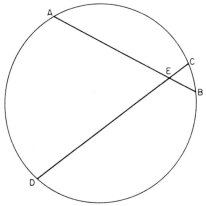

Fig. 4.20

Example 4.6. A pendulum, 2 m in length, swings so that the horizontal distance between extreme positions is 1·5 m. Calculate the vertical height through which the bob rises between its lowest and highest positions. Give the answer in millimetres correct to the nearest millimetre.

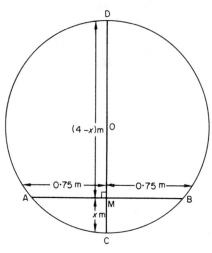

Fig. 4.21

The pendulum is represented in its lowest position by OC and in its highest positions by OA and OB.

Let x metres be the vertical height between the highest and lowest positions; hence $MC = x$ m. Using the theorem of paragraph (i) above,

$$AM \times MB = DM \times MC$$

$$\therefore \ 0·75 \times 0·75 = (4 - x).x$$

$$\therefore \ \frac{9}{16} = 4x - x^2$$

$$\therefore \ 16x^2 - 64x + 9 = 0$$

$$\therefore \ x = \frac{64 \pm \sqrt{64^2 - (4)(9)(16)}}{32}$$

$$= \frac{64 \pm 8\sqrt{64 - 9}}{32}$$

$$= \frac{8 \pm \sqrt{55}}{4}$$

$$= \frac{8 \pm 7 \cdot 416}{4}$$

$$= \frac{15 \cdot 416}{4} \quad \text{or} \quad \frac{0 \cdot 584}{4}$$

$$= 3 \cdot 85 \text{ or } 0 \cdot 146 \text{ m}$$

The larger value is clearly impractical; hence the required value is 146 mm.

4.3   Direct and indirect common tangents to two circles

(a) *Direct*

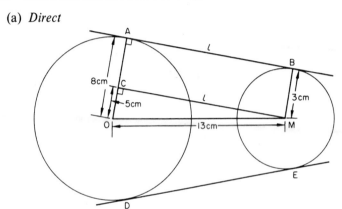

Fig. 4.22

Example 4.7. Calculate the length of a direct common tangent to two circles of radii 8 cm and 3 cm, whose distance between centres is 13 cm.

In Fig. 4.22, AB and DE are direct common tangents of equal length, *l* cm. Draw MC at right-angles to OA; hence MC = *l* and CO = 8 − 3 = 5 cm.

In △COM,

$$l^2 = 13^2 - 5^2$$
$$\therefore l^2 = 169 - 25$$
$$= 144$$
$$\therefore l = 12 \text{ cm}$$

(b) *Indirect*

An indirect tangent, AB, is shown in Fig. 4.23. The construction lines for the calculation of its length are shown in dotted lines BC and MC,

the calculation, using the dimensions of Fig. 4.22, being left to the
student as an exercise. (Ans. 6·92 cm).

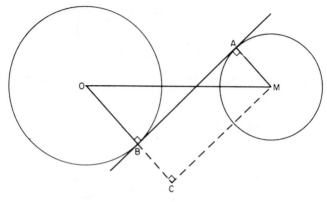

Fig. 4.23

4.4   Sector and segment of a circle

(a) *Sector*

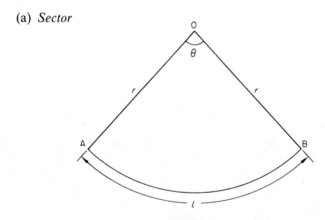

Fig. 4.24

A sector of a circle can be regarded as a fraction of a circle, in respect of
area and length of arc. This fraction is determined by the size of the
angle at the centre; an angle of 60° means $\frac{1}{6}$ of the circle, an angle of
45° means $\frac{1}{8}$ of the circle. A quadrant is a sector of a circle whose angle
at the centre is 90°.

In general,

$$\text{length of arc, } l = \frac{\theta°}{360°} \times 2\pi r$$

and,   area of sector $= \dfrac{\theta°}{360°} \times \pi r^2$

If the angle θ is measured in radians, these formulae become,

$$l = \frac{\theta}{2\pi} \times 2\pi r \qquad \text{and} \qquad \text{area} = \frac{\theta}{2\pi} \times \pi r^2$$

$$\therefore \ l = r\theta \qquad\qquad \therefore \ \text{area} = \tfrac{1}{2}r^2\theta$$

Example 4.8. Calculate the length of a continuous belt in direct drive over two pulleys, radii 3 cm and 8 cm, whose centres are 13 cm apart.

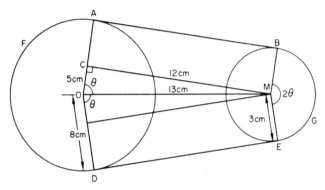

Fig. 4.25

In addition to the two tangents AB and DE, both assumed to be straight, we are required to calculate the two lengths of belt in contact with the pulleys. These are represented by the arcs AFD and BGE of the sectors of circles, OAFD and MBGE. The lengths of these arcs are directly proportional to the angles which they subtend at the centre of each circle, namely, reflex $\angle$ AOD and obtuse $\angle$ BME.

In $\triangle$OCM,

$$\tan \theta = \frac{12}{5} = 2{\cdot}4$$

$$\therefore \ \theta = 67° \ 23'$$

$$\therefore \ 2\theta = 134° \ 46'$$

$$\therefore \ \text{reflex} \ \angle \text{AOD} = 360° - 134° \ 46'$$

$$= 225° \ 14'$$

For practical purposes, this angle can be considered as 225° and therefore the angle BME, i.e., 2θ, is $360° - 225° = 135°$. In this particular problem, the total difference in length of belt, caused by the omission of 14′, is 0·1 cm.

$$\text{arc AFD} = \frac{225}{360} \times 2\pi 8 \text{ cm}$$

$$\text{arc BGE} = \frac{135}{360} \times 2\pi 3 \text{ cm}$$

$$\therefore \text{ arc AFD} + \text{arc BGE} = \frac{225}{360} \times 16\pi + \frac{135}{360} \times 6\pi \text{ cm}$$

$$= 10\pi + \frac{9\pi}{4} \text{ cm}$$

$$= 31\cdot42 + 7\cdot07 \text{ cm}$$

$$= 38\cdot5 \text{ cm}$$

The straight lengths of belt, AB and DE are each 12 cm as was shown in §4.3.

$$\therefore \text{ Total length of belt} = 24 + 38\cdot5 \text{ cm}$$

$$= 62\cdot5 \text{ cm}$$

(b) *Segment*

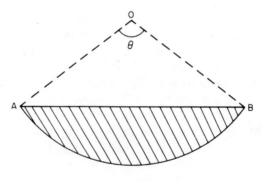

Fig. 4.26

A segment of a circle is the area bounded by a chord and the part of the circumference cut off by the chord. The area is the difference between the area of the corresponding sector and the isosceles triangle OAB in Fig. 4.26. The length of the arc is the same as the length of the arc of the sector.

Example 4.9. Calculate the area of the minor segment cut off by a chord of length 8 cm in a circle of radius 6 cm.

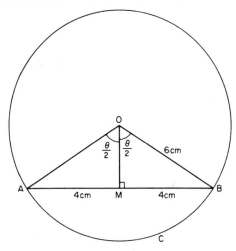

Fig. 4.27

In △MOB,

$$\sin \frac{\theta}{2} = \frac{4}{6} = 0.6667$$

$$\therefore \frac{\theta}{2} = 41° \ 49'$$

$$\therefore \ \angle AOB = \theta = 83° \ 38' = 83.6° \ \text{approx.}$$

Area of segment AMBC = area of sector AOBC − area △AOB

$$= \frac{83.6}{360} \times \pi \times 6^2 - \frac{8 \times OM}{2}$$

$$= \frac{83.6 \times 3.14 \times 36}{360} - 4 \times 6 \cos 41° \ 49'$$

$$= 26.3 - 17.9 \quad \text{(S.R.)}$$

$$= 8.4 \ \text{cm}^2$$

4.5 Standard geometrical constructions

(a) To divide a line of given length into any number of parts whose lengths are in a given proportion.

Example 4.10. Divide a line 8 cm long into three parts whose lengths form the ratio, 2:3:4.

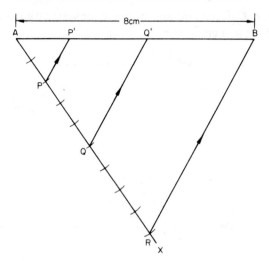

Fig. 4.28

Let the given line be AB. From A, draw a line AX of any convenient length making an angle with AB of 40° to 60° approximately. Along AX, mark off with a pair of compasses, 9 equal distances, (i.e., 2 + 3 + 4). Join the last mark, R, to B and through marks 2(P), and 5(Q), draw lines parallel to RB to cut AB at P' and Q'. The required lengths are then, AP', P'Q' and Q'B.

(b) To construct a tangent to a circle from a point outside the circle.

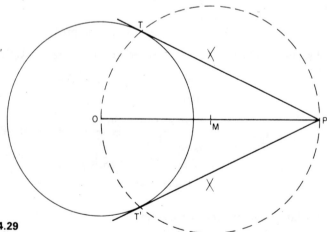

Fig. 4.29

Join the given point P to O, the centre of the circle. Bisect the line OP at M. With M as centre and MO as radius, describe a circle to cut the original circle at T and T'. PT and PT' are then the required tangents.

(c) To construct a direct common tangent to two given circles.

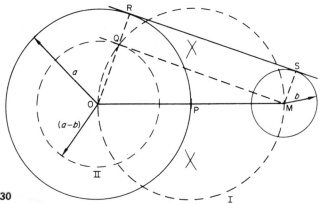

Fig. 4.30

Bisect the line of centres, OM, at P. With centre P and radius PO, draw circle I. With centre O and radius $(a - b)$, draw circle II, intersecting circle I at Q. Join OQ and produce to cut the given circle at R. Through M draw MS parallel to OR, to cut the other given circle at S. RS is then a direct common tangent to the two circles; a second tangent can be found by a similar construction, below the centre line. These two tangents represent the free lengths of an open continuous belt round two pulleys.

(d) To construct an indirect or transverse common tangent to two given circles.

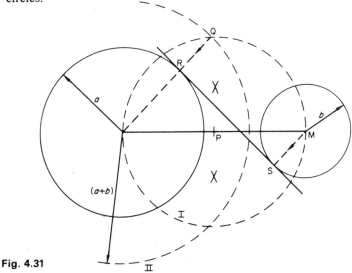

Fig. 4.31

The method of construction is almost identical with the previous one; circle II now has a radius $(a + b)$.

A second tangent can be found, passing over the smaller circle and below the larger. These two tangents represent the free lengths of a crossed continuous belt round two pulleys.

(e) To construct the inscribed circle of a given triangle.

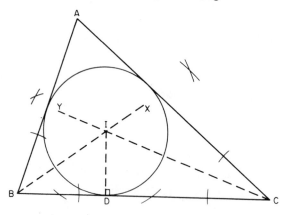

Fig. 4.32

The centre I of the inscribed circle, is the point of intersection of the bisectors BX and CY, of any two of the angles of the triangle; the radius r is the perpendicular ID from I to any side of the triangle.

(f) To construct a circle which circumscribes a given triangle.

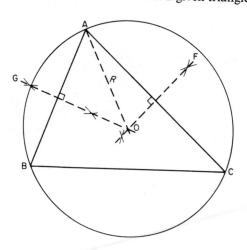

Fig. 4.33

The centre O of the circumscribing circle is the point of intersection of the perpendicular bisectors, OF and OG, of any two sides of the triangle; the radius R is the length OA or OB or OC.

(g) To construct a continuous smooth curve having more than one radius of curvature.

Example 4.11. Draw Fig. 4.34, full size, showing all necessary construction lines. The arcs of the two circles join smoothly and are tangential to the two vertical lines.

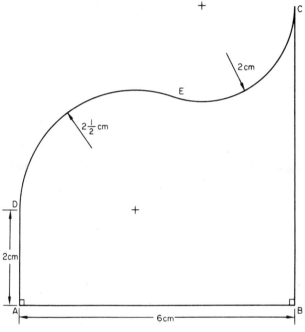

Fig. 4.34

Analysis

The method requires an application of the theorem shown in Figs. 4.12 and 4.13, showing external and internal contact of two circles. The two arcs are parts of two circles which are in external contact, say at E, which therefore lies on the line of centres; distance apart of centres = $(2\frac{1}{2} + 2)$ cm.

If AD is a tangent to one circle, the centre will lie on a line through D, at right-angles to AD at a distance of $2\frac{1}{2}$ cm.

The same construction cannot be applied to the other centre since the position of C is not known. The centre of this smaller circle will lie on a line parallel to BC, distant 2 cm.

Construction

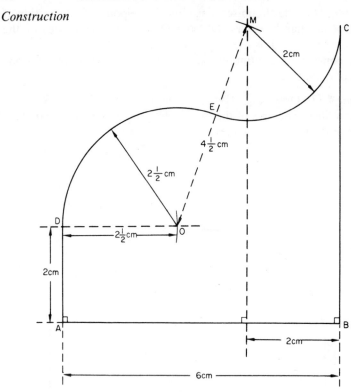

Fig. 4.35

Example 4.12. Draw Fig. 4.36 full size, showing all necessary construction lines. The arcs of the two circles join smoothly, say at C. AB is a tangent to the arc at B and the tangent to the arc at D is at right-angles to AD.

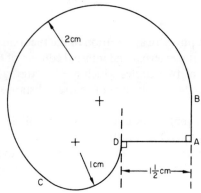

Fig. 4.36

Analysis

The centres of the two arcs being on the same side of the curve indicates that the two circles have internal contact.

Distance between centres $= 2 - 1 = 1$ cm, and C, the point of contact, lies on the line of centres. If AB is a tangent to the larger circle at B, then the centre lies on a line parallel to AB, distant 2 cm.

If the tangent to the smaller circle at D is at right-angles to AD, then AD produced must pass through the centre of the circle at a distance of 1 cm from D.

Construction

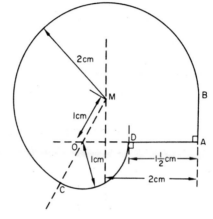

Fig. 4.37

(h) To construct a regular polygon of given length of side.

The method of construction depends on the theorem which states that equal chords in a circle subtend equal angles at the centre. Hence, each side of a square inscribed in a circle, will subtend 90° at the centre of the circle.

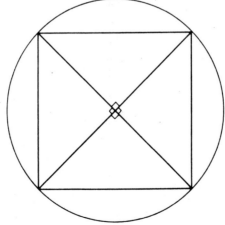

Fig. 4.38

Each side of a regular hexagon will subtend 60° at the centre of the circle.

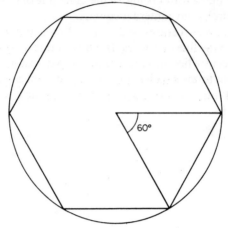

Fig. 4.39

The angles, 60° and 90°, having simple standard constructions, form the basis of the method for all other polygons.

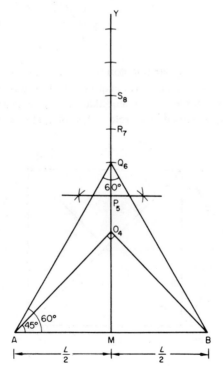

Fig. 4.40

Method

Let the given length of side be L units. Draw this line AB and construct the perpendicular bisector, MY.

At A, construct an angle of 45° meeting MY at O_4.

At A, construct an angle of 60° meeting MY at Q_6.

Since $AO_4B = 90°$, and $AQ_6B = 60°$, then O_4 and Q_6 are the centres of circles in which can be inscribed regular polygons of 4 and 6 sides respectively, of length L units each. Bisect the length O_4Q_6 at P_5; mark off along MY, R_7, S_8, etc., at distances equal to O_4P_5 and P_5Q_6. The points, P_5, R_7, S_8, etc., are then the centres of circles which will contain regular inscribed polygons of 5, 7, and 8 sides of length L units.

The required polygon is completed by marking out the length L as successive chords of the appropriate circle.

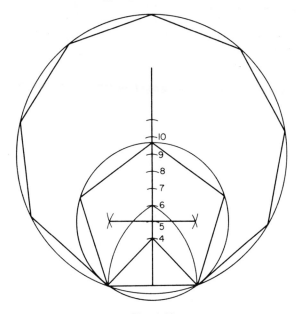

Fig. 4.41

(i) Principle of centring gauge.

One type of centring gauge is shown in Fig. 4.42. It is made of metal about 3 mm thickness with pegs at A and B approximately 12 mm in length. The straight edge DC, if produced, would bisect the line AB at right-angles. If the gauge is applied to the arc whose centre is required, the pegs A and B locate on the arc, making the line AB a chord of the circle; hence, CD, the perpendicular bisector of the chord, passes

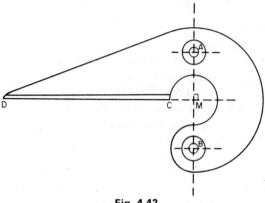

Fig. 4.42

through the centre of the circular arc. If this line CD is marked, and the gauge applied in a second position, the intersection of the two lines, CD, will be the actual centre of the circle.

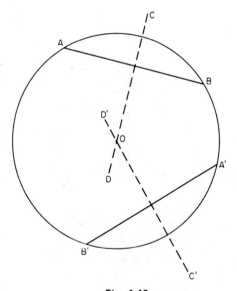

Fig. 4.43

EXERCISE 4.1

1. Calculate the lengths of chords, whose distances from the centre of a circle of radius 170 mm are (a) 80 mm, (b) 120 mm, (c) 140 mm.

2. Calculate the radii of circles in which chords of length 160 mm are at the following distances from the centres: (a) 150 mm, (b) 80 mm, (c) 45 mm.

3. Calculate the distances from the centres of circles of radii 100 mm of chords whose lengths are (a) 160 mm, (b) 120 mm, (c) 90 mm.

4.

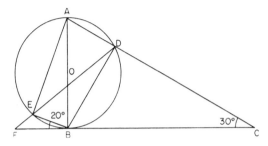

Fig. 4.44

In Fig. 4.44, calculate the sizes of the following angles, given that O is the centre of the circle and that CBF is a tangent at B:

(a) EDB	(b) EAB	(c) ADE	(d) DBC
(e) DAB	(f) DEB	(g) AED	(h) ABE
(i) ABD	(j) AOD		

5. Calculate the lengths of tangents to a circle of radius 40 mm, drawn from a point 80 mm from the centre.

6. Tangents to a circle of radius 150 mm are drawn from a point 650 mm from the centre. Calculate the length of the chord of contact.

7. Two equal circles, radius 200 mm, are inscribed in a rectangle measuring 800 mm by 400 mm. Calculate the radius of another circle which touches the two equal circles and also touches the long side of the rectangle.

8. Calculate the radius of a circle which can be inscribed in a quadrant of another circle whose radius is 100 mm.

9. Two equal spheres of radius 30 mm rest inside a cylinder of height 100 mm as shown in Fig. 4.45. Calculate the diameter of the cylinder.

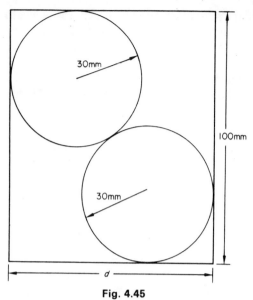

Fig. 4.45

10. The end section of a shaft of a motor is in the form of a major arc of a circle of radius 4 cm cut off by a chord of length 4 cm. Calculate the area of the section.

U.E.I. (part Qn.)

11. The radius of the arc of a circular segment is 60 mm and the angle subtended by it at the centre is 35°. Calculate, taking π as $\frac{22}{7}$,

   (a) the area of the segment,

   (b) the length of the chord,

   (c) the distance of the chord from the centre of the circle.

E.M.E.U.

12. In Fig. 4.46, OA and OB are common tangents to the two circles which also touch each other. If the radii are r and R respectively, deduce that,

$$\sin \frac{\theta}{2} = \frac{R - r}{R + r}$$

and hence determine the value of R given that $\theta = 20°$ and $r = 15$ mm.

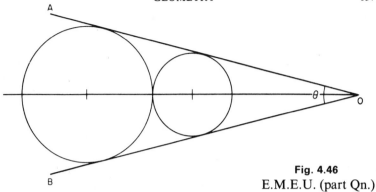

Fig. 4.46
E.M.E.U. (part Qn.)

13. Two tangents to a circle, 60 mm in diameter, intersect at a point 50 mm from the centre of the circle. Find the lengths of the tangents and the angle between them.

N.C.T.E.C. (part Qn.)

14. Figure 4.47 shows a right-angle bend in a road with $AB = BC = a$ metres (the radius of a circle with centre O). The road is to be modified as shown by the dotted lines to remove the sharp corner. If the width of the road is x metres, show that the saving in road surface area of the modification is given by,

$$\left(1 - \frac{\pi}{4}\right)(2ax - x^2) \text{ m}^2$$

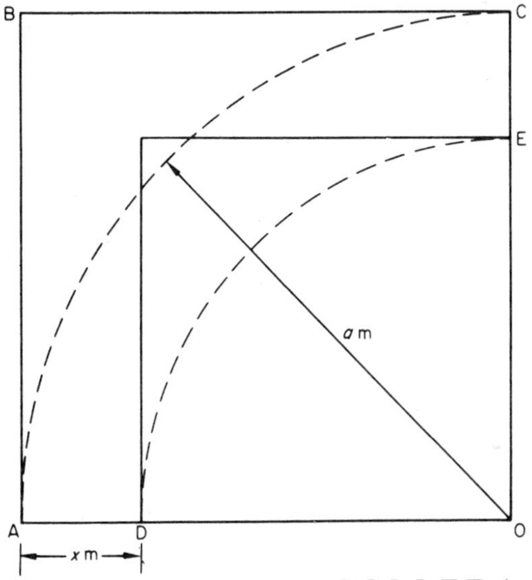

Fig. 4.47   C.G.L.I. T.T. (part Qn.)

15. (a) An annulus is formed by two concentric circles of radii 60 mm and 50 mm. Calculate the area of that part of the annulus which lies between two radii inclined at 54° to one another.

   (b) AB is a diameter of a circle of radius 50 mm and AK is a chord 85 mm long. The tangent to the circle at B and the chord AK produced meet at D. Calculate, (a) the length of the chord, BK, (b) the angle KBD, (c) the distance of the mid-point of BK from the centre of the circle.

C.G.L.I. E.T.

16. (a) Two intersecting circles of diameters 18·5 cm and 10 cm have a common chord 6 cm long. Calculate the distance between the centres of the circles.

   (b) AB is a chord of a circle of radius 140 mm. AT and BT are tangents to the circles at A and B respectively and meet in T. The centre of the circle is the point O and angle BAT = 65°. BK is a diameter. Calculate, (i) angle BKA. (ii) angle KBA, (iii) length of BT, (iv) area of the quadrilateral AOBT.

C.G.L.I. E.T.

17. A sector of a circle has arc length $5\pi/6$ and area $5\pi/2$. Calculate the radius and the angle in degrees enclosed by the sector at the centre of the circle.

C.G.L.I. T.T. (part Qn.)

18. A sector of a circle radius r contains an angle θ radians at the centre of the circle. If the total perimeter of the sector is 12 m find a formula connecting r and θ and show that the area A of the sector is given by $A = 6r - r^2$.

   Find with the aid of a graph, the maximum value of A, and the values of r and θ corresponding to this maximum.

C.G.L.I. T.T.

19. In Fig. 4.48 the point O is the centre of a circle of radius 50 mm. AB is a chord of the circle and the tangents to the circle at A and B meet in T, such that the angle ATB = 48°. AD is a diameter.

   (a) Determine (i) angle ADB, (ii) length of chord AB, (iii) area of the quadrilateral ADBT.

   (b) If the same figure were drawn with a circle of radius 100 mm, state what would then be the values of those three results.

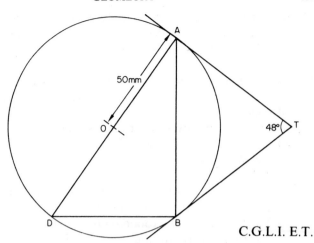

Fig. 4.48

C.G.L.I. E.T.

20. A belt passes round a pulley of radius 40 mm. If 80 mm of the belt is in contact with the pulley, calculate the angle at the centre of the pulley subtended by this portion of the belt in (a) radians, (b) degrees.

U.E.I. (part Qn.)

21. (a) Convert 300° into radians.
   (b) A sector of a circle of radius 100 mm subtends an angle of 300° at the centre. Calculate (i) the length of the arc of the sector, (ii) the area of the sector.

U.L.C.I.

22. In Fig. 4.49 AB is a diameter of a circle centre D. From a point O on BA produced a tangent is drawn to meet the circle at C.
   (a) If OC = 120 mm and OD = 130 mm, find the radius of the circle and the angle OCA.
   (b) The maximum power factor under which an induction motor can operate is given by the ratio CD/OD. If $x = OA/OB$, show that the maximum power factor

$$CD/OD = (1 - x)/(1 + x)$$

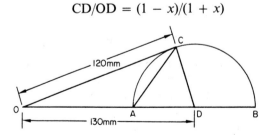

Fig. 4.49

Y.C.

23. A diameter AB of a circle is produced to a point T and a tangent
    TC is drawn to touch the circle at C. Calculate the angles TAC
    and TBC if the angle ATC = 40°.

                                                    Y.C. (part Qn.)

24. Two circles of diameters, 78 mm and 50 mm respectively, intersect
    at A and B. If their common chord AB has a length of 30 mm,
    calculate,
    (a) the distance between their centres C and D,
    (b) the area of the triangle CAD,
    (c) the angle CAD.

                                                    Y.C. (part Qn.)

25. (a) The arc of a sector of a circle of radius 20 mm subtends an
        angle $2\pi/3$ radians at the centre. Calculate the area of the sector.
    (b) Two friction wheels rotate on fixed axles, make contact at P
        and roll together without slipping. (Fig. 4.50.) Calculate the
        number of revolutions made by the smaller wheel when the
        larger rotates through an angle of $\pi/3$ radians.

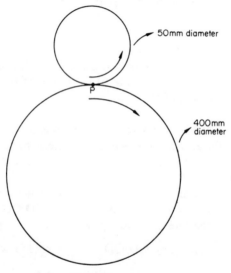

50mm diameter

400mm
diameter

Fig. 4.50   U.L.C.I.

26. A blade of an electric fan is a sector of a circle of radius 250 mm and
    has an area of 23,200 mm². Calculate,
    (a) the angle of the sector in degrees and minutes,
    (b) determine the speed in m/s of a point on the arc of the blade
        when the fan is rotating at 200 rev/min.

                                                    C.G.L.I. E.T. (part Qn.)

27. A circle of 50 mm radius, centre at point P, intersects another circle of 100 mm radius, centre at point Q. A common chord AB is drawn through the points of intersection and is 50 mm long. Draw a sketch and calculate the area of the quadrilateral PAQB.

U.L.C.I.

28. Draw Fig. 4.51 full size, given that all arcs join smoothly and that AB is tangential to arcs at A and B. Show all construction lines.

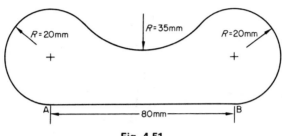

Fig. 4.51

29. Draw Fig. 4.52 full size, given that all arcs join smoothly and that AB, CD and EF are tangents. OA = 50 mm.

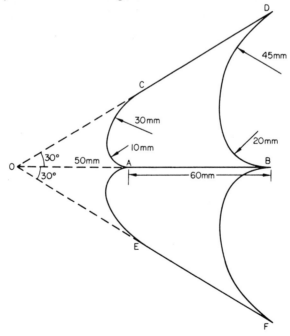

Fig. 4.52

30. The boundary of the diagram in Fig. 4.53 consists of the arcs of
   four circles, FED, DCB, BAG, and GHF, which join smoothly
   at D and B but not at G and F. The radii of FED and BAG are
   each 20 mm, that of DCB 60 mm and that of GHF 15 mm. HM is
   5 mm and the centre of BCD lies on EA. Draw the diagram full
   size showing all construction lines.

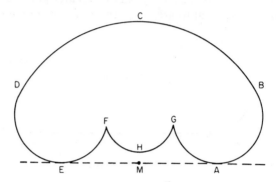

Fig. 4.53

31. Construct to a scale $\frac{3}{8}$ full size a triangle of sides 120 mm, 140 mm,
   and 160 mm. Draw the inscribed and circumscribed circles for this
   triangle, showing clearly in each case how the centre of the circle is
   located.   C.G.L.I. T.T.

32. Draw Fig. 4.54 full size, showing all construction lines for obtaining
   the centres of arcs and also for finding the points at which arcs and
   lines join.

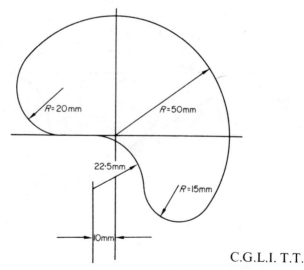

Fig. 4.54   C.G.L.I. T.T.

33. Draw an angle ABC = 60°. Draw a circle 40 mm diameter between the arms of this angle in such a position that this circle touches the line BC and cuts the line AB at two points 10 mm apart.

Note. Full marks may be obtained for this question *only* by a solution involving a geometric construction for the location of the circle centre. C.G.L.I. T.T.

34. The plan of a bracket is shown in Fig. 4.55. Draw this full size, showing clearly all construction marks.

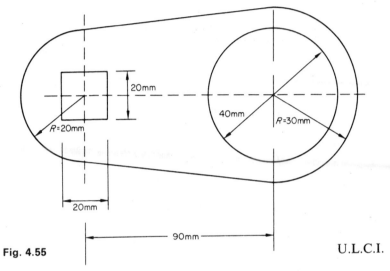

Fig. 4.55 U.L.C.I.

35. A template is to be made a regular pentagon as shown in Fig. 4.56. Show how you would mark out this template from a flat piece of metal using only dividers, rule and scriber. Leave all construction lines clearly visible.

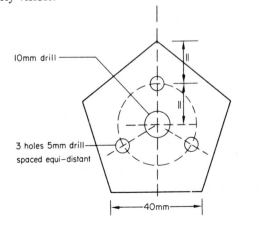

Fig. 4.56 U.L.C.I.

36. The cover plate for a junction box is shown in plan in Fig. 4.57. Draw this view, full size, showing clearly all construction marks.

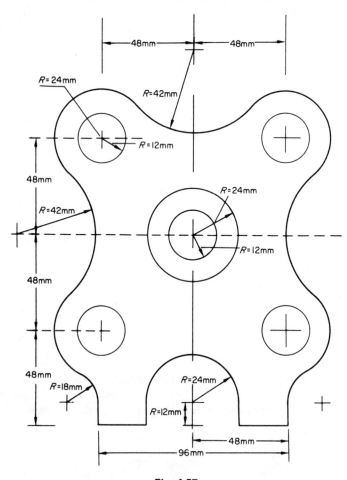

Fig. 4.57

U.L.C.I. (part Qn.)

37. Figure 4.58 shows a simple link mechanism. The point C of the lever CE is constrained to move along AB; it is allowed to pivot about and slide through the fixed point D. Draw full size the path of the end of the lever E when the point C moves along AB from one extreme to the other. The length CE is 114 mm and the distance CD is 27 mm.

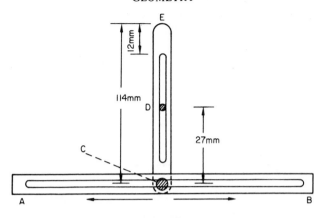

Fig. 4.58

38. Figure 4.59 shows a simple link mechanism. The crank OA revolves about O at constant speed. Plot the path of the point R for one revolution of OA. The end B of the rod is constrained to move along PQ. OA = 0·5 m, AB = 1·55 m, and AR = 1·125 m. Scale, 1:20.

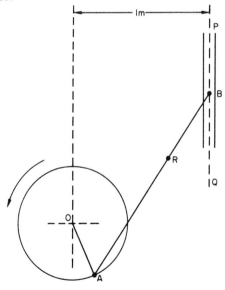

Fig. 4.59

39. Figure 4.60 shows the plan of a pair of folding doors. Plot the path of the point P for the full movement of A from D to C. AB and BC are each 2 m and AP is 0·8 m.
Scale, 1:10.

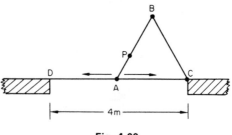

Fig. 4.60

U.L.C.I.

40. In Fig. 4.61 two links OA and AB, 90 mm and 40 mm long respectively, are freely pin-jointed at A and OA can rotate freely about O. OA and AB are able to move in the plane OPQ as B slides along PQ perpendicular to OP. If B commences at P and has a total movement of 70 mm, draw full size, the locus, i.e., the path, of the centre of the link AB by taking the positions of B at intervals of 10 mm.

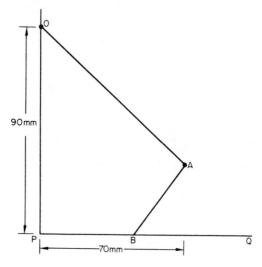

Fig. 4.61

U.L.C.I.

41. The linkage of a special purpose mechanism is shown in Fig. 4.62. The crank OA rotates in an anticlockwise direction about the centre O. A rigid connecting rod AC is connected to the crank by means of a pin at A. The end C is constrained to slide along the line XX. An arm is rigidly connected to the crank at B. Draw full size, the path of the point P for one revolution of the crank.

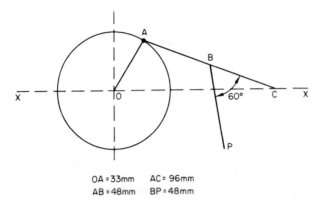

OA = 33mm   AC = 96mm
AB = 48mm   BP = 48mm

Fig. 4.62

U.L.C.I.

5. Trigonometry

5.1 Further trigonometrical ratios

In Vol. 1, the ratios of the sides of a right-angled triangle were used to illustrate the values of three trigonometrical ratios.

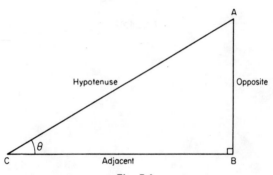

Fig. 5.1

$$\sin \theta = \frac{AB}{AC}, \quad \cos \theta = \frac{BC}{AC}, \quad \tan \theta = \frac{AB}{BC}$$

Three other ratios, which form the reciprocals of sine, cosine, and tangent, can now be stated:

$$\text{cosecant } \theta \text{ (abbreviation cosec } \theta) = \frac{1}{\sin \theta}$$

$$\text{secant } \theta \text{ (abbreviation sec } \theta) = \frac{1}{\cos \theta}$$

$$\text{cotangent } \theta \text{ (abbreviation cot } \theta) = \frac{1}{\tan \theta}$$

If the appropriate tables are available, there is an advantage in using cosecant or secant, when it is required to calculate the length of the hypotenuse of a right-angled triangle.

In Fig. 5.1,

$$\frac{AC}{AB} = \text{cosec } \theta, \qquad \frac{AC}{BC} = \sec \theta, \qquad \frac{BC}{AB} = \cot \theta$$

5.2 Sine, cosine, and tangent of angles of any magnitude; period of a function

An angle is the name given to a measurement of rotation and can have all values, either positive or negative. It is misleading to consider its size to be restricted to the values of angles which form parts of triangles, quadrilaterals, polygons, etc.

We consider in the figures following, angles in the four quadrants of a circle, in the four ranges of values, 0–90°, 90–180°, 180–270°, and 270–360°.

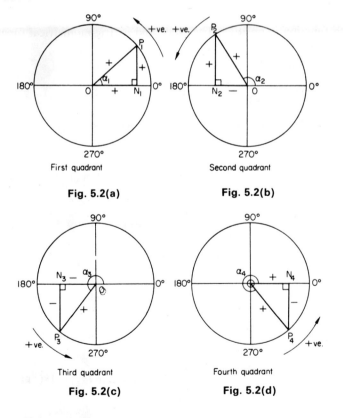

First quadrant

Fig. 5.2(a)

Second quadrant

Fig. 5.2(b)

Third quadrant

Fig. 5.2(c)

Fourth quadrant

Fig. 5.2(d)

A radius OP, rotating in an anticlockwise direction, which by definition we take as a positive rotation, passes through the positions OP_1, OP_2, OP_3, and OP_4, representing angular movements of α_1, α_2, α_3, α_4. In each of these positions, P_1N_1, P_2N_2, P_3N_3, and P_4N_4 are drawn at right-angles to the initial (0°) line. The lengths of the sides of the triangles thus formed are given the positive and negative signs of measurement which are defined by the x and y graphical axes; the arm OP which becomes the hypotenuse of each triangle, is positive in all positions, by definition.

(a) First quadrant, 0–90°

$$\sin \alpha_1 = \frac{P_1N_1}{OP_1}$$

$$\cos \alpha_1 = \frac{ON_1}{OP_1}$$

$$\tan \alpha_1 = \frac{PN_1}{ON_1}$$

Each function is positive. The angle and its trigonometrical function can be read directly in tables.

(b) Second quadrant, 90–180°

$$\sin \alpha_2 = \frac{+P_2N_2}{+OP_2} = \sin P_2ON_2 = \sin (180° - \alpha_2)$$

$$\cos \alpha_2 = \frac{-ON_2}{+OP_2} = -\cos P_2ON_2 = -\cos (180° - \alpha_2)$$

$$\tan \alpha_2 = \frac{+P_2N_2}{-ON_2} = -\tan P_2ON_2 = -\tan (180° - \alpha_2)$$

Example 5.1.

$$\cos 130° = -\cos (180° - 130°) = -\cos 50°$$
$$= -0{\cdot}6428$$

(c) Third quadrant, 180–270°

$$\sin \alpha_3 = \frac{-P_3N_3}{+OP_3} = -\sin P_3ON_3 = -\sin (\alpha_3 - 180°)$$

$$\cos \alpha_3 = \frac{-ON_3}{+OP_3} = -\cos P_3ON_3 = -\cos (\alpha_3 - 180°)$$

$$\tan \alpha_3 = \frac{-P_3N_3}{-ON_3} = +\tan P_3ON_3 = \tan (\alpha_3 - 180°)$$

Example 5.2.

$$\sin 210° = -\sin (210° - 180°) = -\sin 30°$$
$$= -0.5000$$

(d) Fourth quadrant, 270–360°

$$\sin \alpha_4 = \frac{-P_4N_4}{+OP_4} = -\sin P_4ON_4 = -\sin (360° - \alpha_4)$$

$$\cos \alpha_4 = \frac{+ON_4}{+OP_4} = +\cos P_4ON_4 = \cos (360° - \alpha_4)$$

$$\tan \alpha_4 = \frac{-P_4N_4}{+ON_4} = -\tan P_4ON_4 = -\tan (360° - \alpha_4)$$

Example 5.3.

$$\tan 320° = -\tan (360° - 320°) = -\tan 40°$$
$$= 0.8391$$

One rotation of the radius OP covers all possible changes in the values of sine, cosine, and tangent of angle α; further rotation will repeat these values.

Example 5.4.

$$\sin 400° = \sin (400° - 360°) = \sin 40°$$
$$\cos 500° = \cos (500° - 360°) = \cos 140° = -\cos 40°$$
$$\tan 600° = \tan (600° - 360°) = \tan 240° = \tan 60°$$

Functions of this type are said to be 'cyclical'; the range of values of the angle over which one cycle of values of the function is completed is called the 'period' of the function. Hence the period of $\sin \alpha$, $\cos \alpha$, and $\tan \alpha$ is 360° or 2π radians; strictly speaking, this quantity should read, 360° per cycle, or 2π radians per cycle, but this has been implied in the meaning of the word 'period'.

Negative angles

If the arm OP rotates in a clockwise direction, the angle so formed is said to be negative. In each position of OP, we construct the same series of triangles, OPN, as before; the trigonometrical functions of negative angles thus depend only on the position of OP and not on its direction of rotation.

Example 5.5. $-30°$

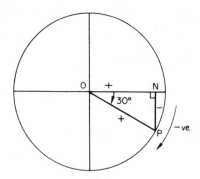

Fig. 5.3(i)

$$\sin(-30°) = \frac{-PN}{OP} = -\sin 30°$$

$$\cos(-30°) = \frac{ON}{OP} = \cos 30°$$

$$\tan(-30°) = \frac{-PN}{ON} = -\tan 30°$$

Example 5.6. $-130°$

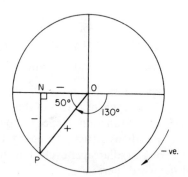

Fig. 5.3(ii)

$$\sin(-130°) = \frac{-PN}{OP} = -\sin 50°$$

$$\cos(-130°) = \frac{-ON}{OP} = -\cos 50°$$

$$\tan(-130°) = \frac{-PN}{-ON} = +\tan 50°$$

Example 5.7. $-240°$

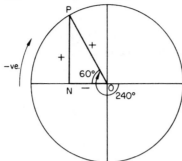

Fig. 5.3(iii)

$$\sin(-240°) = \frac{PN}{OP} = \sin 60°$$

$$\cos(-240°) = \frac{-ON}{OP} = -\cos 60°$$

$$\tan(-240°) = \frac{PN}{-ON} = -\tan 60°$$

Example 5.8. $-320°$

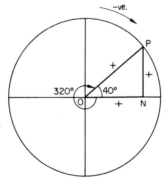

Fig. 5.3(iv)

$$\sin(-320°) = \frac{PN}{OP} = \sin 40°$$

$$\cos(-320°) = \frac{ON}{OP} = \cos 40°$$

$$\tan(-320°) = \frac{PN}{ON} = \tan 40°$$

Boundary values; sine, cosine, and tangent of 0, $\pi/2$, π, $3\pi/2$, 2π **radians**

Considering the four diagrams of Fig. 5.4, special values of sine, cosine, and tangent of α will arise when the radius OP coincides with the boundary between any two quadrants.

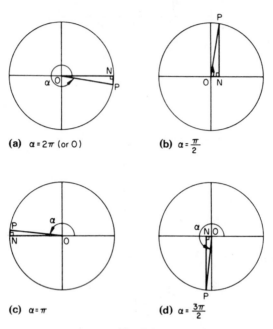

(a) $\alpha = 2\pi$ (or 0)   **(b)** $\alpha = \dfrac{\pi}{2}$

(c) $\alpha = \pi$ **(d)** $\alpha = \dfrac{3\pi}{2}$

Fig. 5.4

In each of the four diagrams of Fig. 5.4, the radius OP has been drawn close to the boundaries between quadrants. When OP coincides with a boundary, one side of the triangle OPN will become zero length and the other two sides will then be equal in length.

(a) When $\alpha = 2\pi$ (or 0), PN = 0 and ON = OP

$$\sin 2\pi = \frac{PN}{OP} = 0 = \sin 0$$

$$\cos 2\pi = \frac{ON}{OP} = 1 = \cos 0$$

$$\tan 2\pi = \frac{PN}{ON} = 0 = \tan 0$$

(b) When $\alpha = \dfrac{\pi}{2}$, ON = 0 and OP = PN

$$\sin \frac{\pi}{2} = \frac{PN}{OP} = 1$$

$$\cos \frac{\pi}{2} = \frac{ON}{OP} = 0$$

$$\tan \frac{\pi}{2} = \frac{PN}{ON} = \frac{PN}{0} = \infty$$

The symbol ∞, referred to as 'infinity', or 'an infinitely large number', is the result of dividing the length of PN by zero.

(c) When $\alpha = \pi$, PN = 0 and ON = OP

$$\sin \pi = \frac{PN}{OP} = 0$$

$$\cos \pi = \frac{ON}{OP} = -1$$

$$\tan \pi = \frac{PN}{OP} = 0$$

(d) When $\alpha = \dfrac{3\pi}{2}$, ON = 0 and OP = PN

$$\sin \frac{3\pi}{2} = \frac{PN}{OP} = -1$$

$$\cos \frac{3\pi}{2} = \frac{ON}{OP} = 0$$

$$\tan \frac{3\pi}{2} = \frac{PN}{ON} = -\infty$$

5.3 Graphs of sine, cosine, and tangent

The results of §5.2 are important and can be seen and used to better advantage by means of graphical presentation. A clear understanding of these basic graphs will be of immense assistance to the student in many problems and principles of a.c. theory.

(a) sin θ for values of θ, 0–2π radians

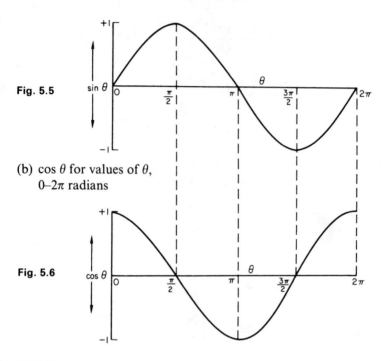

Fig. 5.5

(b) cos θ for values of θ,
    0–2π radians

Fig. 5.6

Period
The graphs of sin θ and cos θ each have a period of 2π radians; note
that this is a value of θ.

Amplitude
The amplitude of a function is the numerical value of its variation on
each side of zero; the amplitude of both sin θ and cos θ is 1.

(c) tan θ for values of θ, 0–2π radians

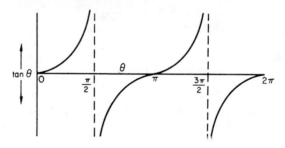

Fig. 5.7

(d) Compare $\sin \theta$ and $\sin 2\theta$

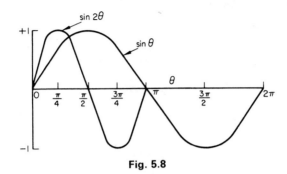

Fig. 5.8

    (i) the amplitudes of the two functions are the same, i.e., 1
    (ii) the period of $\sin 2\theta$ is π radians

(e) Compare $\sin \theta$ and $2 \sin \theta$

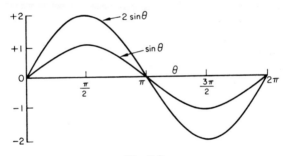

Fig. 5.9

    (i) the periods of the two functions are the same, i.e., 2π radians
    (ii) the amplitude of $2 \sin \theta$ is 2

It is clear from Figs. 5.8 and 5.9, that there is a considerable difference in the effect of the factor 2 in $\sin 2\theta$ and $2 \sin \theta$.

Example 5.9. If $\theta = 35°$,

$$\sin 2\theta = \sin 2 \times 35° = \sin 70° = 0\cdot9397$$

and $2 \sin \theta = 2 \sin 35° = 2 \times 0\cdot5736 = 1\cdot1472$

In general, the period of $R \sin (n\theta)$ is $2\pi/n$, and its amplitude is R.

EXERCISE 5.1

1. From tables, read the values of:

   (a) sin 115°   (b) cos 165°
   (c) tan 142°   (d) sin 205°
   (e) tan 230°   (f) cos 260°
   (g) sin 300°   (h) cos 320°
   (i) tan 340°   (j) cos 1000°

2. From trigonometrical tables and reciprocal tables, read the values of:

   (a) sec 20°   (b) cosec 100°
   (c) cotan 215°   (d) sec 305°
   (e) $-$cosec 75°   (f) $-$cotan 120°
   (g) $-$sec 235°   (h) cosec 380°
   (i) cotan 570°   (j) sec 125°

3. Evaluate the following, using tables:

   (a) $\cos 3\theta$ where $\theta = 25°$
   (b) $4 \sin \theta$ where $\theta = 117°$
   (c) $3 \tan 2\theta$ where $\theta = 200°$
   (d) $\frac{1}{2} \sin 2\theta$ where $\theta = 40°$
   (e) $\sin \frac{1}{2}\theta + \cos \frac{1}{2}\theta$ where $\theta = 220°$
   (f) $2 \sin \theta \cos \theta$ where $\theta = 195°$
   (g) $\dfrac{2 \sin \theta}{\sin 2\theta}$ where $\theta = 312°$
   (h) $\cosec 2\theta + \dfrac{2}{\cotan 2\theta}$ where $\theta = 105°$
   (i) $\sec 3\theta \tan \frac{1}{3}\theta$ where $\theta = 120°$
   (j) $-2 \cos \theta$ where $\theta = 180°$

4. Draw the graph of $y = \sin \theta$, for values of θ from 0° to 360° at intervals of 30°. From your graph, find, (a) the value of $\sin \theta$ when $\theta = 220°$, (b) the values of θ when $\sin \theta = -0.75$.

5. Draw the graph of $\cos \theta$, for values of θ from 0 to 2π radians, at intervals of $\pi/6$ radians. From your graph, find, (a) the value of $\cos \theta$, when $\theta = 7\pi/12$ radians, (b) the values of θ, when $\cos \theta = 0.65$.

6. Draw the graph of $y = 3 \sin 2\theta$ for values of θ from 0 to π radians at intervals of $\pi/12$ radians. State the period and amplitude of $3 \sin 2\theta$.

7. Draw the graph of $y = 2 \cos 3\theta$ for values of θ from 0 to $\frac{2}{3}\pi$ radians at intervals of $\pi/12$ radians. State the period and amplitude of $2 \cos 3\theta$.

8. Draw on the same scale and axes, the graphs of $y = 2 \sin \theta$ and $y = 3 \cos \theta$ for values of θ from 0 to 2π radians at intervals of $\pi/6$ radians. Read the values of θ at the points of intersection of the graphs, and, by use of tables, verify that these values are solutions of the equation, $2 \sin \theta = 3 \cos \theta$.

9. By drawing two suitable graphs on the same scale and axes, solve graphically, the equation $\sin \theta - \cos \theta = 0$ for solutions between 0 and 2π radians.

10. A sine function has an amplitude of 4 and a period of π radians. Write down an expression for the function in terms of θ and plot the graph over a whole period.

5.4. Period, frequency, angular velocity

The period of a function has already been explained in respect of $\sin \theta$ and $\cos \theta$ as being 2π radians, i.e., a measurement of the angle θ. This is comparable with stating that the period of service on a motorway is 1 km, i.e., a linear measurement compared with an angle measurement θ. The terms frequency and velocity introduce an element of time, e.g., a lighthouse flashes three times per minute or a vehicle is travelling at 60 km/h.

A velocity of rotation can be given in rev/s; this would be equivalent to a statement of frequency, e.g., 50 rev/s. Since one complete revolution represents an angular measurement of 2π radians, then 50 rev/s is equivalent to $50 \times 2\pi$ radians/s; this is a statement of angular velocity.

The measurement of a period of a function is the range in which one complete cycle of values occurs. Using the frequency of rotation, 50 rev/s, we require to find the time in which 1 revolution occurs, i.e., $\frac{1}{50}$ sec, which is the period, T.

Hence, a frequency of 50 rev/s, an angular velocity of 100π rad/s and a time period of $\frac{1}{50}$ sec are equivalent measures of rotation.

In general, a frequency of f Hz, an angular velocity of $2\pi f$ rad/s and a time period of $(1/f)$s, are equivalent measures of rotation. Hence, the angle θ, turned through in t s at a frequency of f Hz is $2\pi ft$ radians. The symbol ω (omega) is used for angular velocity, replacing $2\pi f$ rad/s; hence,

$$\theta = 2\pi ft = \omega t$$

Figure 9.12 of Vol. 1 showed the sine curve produced by a rotating radius OP on a base of angle measurement. The same diagram is now repeated, Fig. 5.10, on a time base.

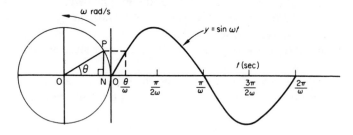

Fig. 5.10

The radius OP rotates at a constant angular velocity of ω rad/s, hence the time taken to turn through

$$\theta, \frac{\pi}{2}, \pi, \frac{3\pi}{2} \text{ and } 2\pi \text{ radians}$$

will be,

$$\frac{\theta}{\omega}, \frac{\pi}{2\omega}, \frac{\pi}{\omega}, \frac{3\pi}{2\omega} \text{ and } \frac{2\pi}{\omega} \text{ sec}$$

respectively.

The graph represents,

$$y = \sin \theta$$

or

$$y = \sin 2\pi ft$$

or

$$y = \sin \omega t$$

The period, $T = 2\pi/\omega$ sec.

Example 5.10. Period $T = \frac{1}{60}$ sec, $\therefore$ frequency = 60 Hz. If the radius OP of Fig. 5.10 rotates under these conditions for a time of 0·04 sec, it will turn through an angle of $120\pi \times 0·04$ radians, i.e., $4·8\,\pi$ radians, which is 864°: in this position we can evaluate each of its trigonometrical functions as those of 144°, i.e., 864° − 720°.

Example 5.11. Evaluate $\sin \omega t$, if $\omega = 40$ rad/s and $t = 0·1$ sec.

$$\sin \omega t = \sin (40 \times 0·1) = \sin (4 \text{ radians}) = \sin (4 \times 57·3°)$$
$$= \sin 229·2° = -\sin (229·2° - 180°)$$
$$= -\sin 49·2° = -0·7570$$

Example 5.12. Evaluate $\cos 2\pi ft$, if $f = 100$ Hz and $t = 0.012$ sec.

$$\begin{aligned}
\cos 2\pi ft &= \cos (2\pi \times 100 \times 0.012) \\
&= \cos 2.4\pi \\
&= \cos (2.4 \times 180°) \\
&= \cos 432° \\
&= \cos (432° - 360°) \\
&= \cos 72° \\
&= 0.3090
\end{aligned}$$

Example 5.13. A quantity which is a sine function has an amplitude of 10 and a frequency of 40. Write down an expression for the function in terms of t, where t is in sec.

Let
$$y = F(t) = R \sin 2\pi ft$$
$$\therefore y = 10 \sin 2\pi \times 40 \times t$$
$$= 10 \sin 80\,\pi t$$

Example 5.14. If $y = \sin 300t$, where t is in sec, write down the period and frequency of y.

From $y = \sin 2\pi ft$ it follows that $2\pi f = 300$; hence $f = (300/2\pi)$ Hz and period $T = 1/f = (2\pi/300)$ sec.

Example 5.15. The value of an alternating current, iA, in a circuit, after time t sec is given by, $i = 50 \sin 100\,\pi t$. Calculate, (a) the time when the current first reaches 25A, (b) the value of the current after 0.055 sec.

(a)
$$50 \sin 100\,\pi t = i$$
$$\therefore 50 \sin 100\,\pi t = 25$$
$$\therefore \sin 100\,\pi t = 25/50 = 0.5$$
$$\therefore 100\,\pi t = \pi/6, \quad \text{since } \sin \pi/6 = 0.5$$
$$\therefore t = \tfrac{1}{600} = 0.00166 \text{ sec}$$

(b)
$$i = 50 \sin 100\,\pi t$$
$$\therefore i = 50 \sin (100\,\pi \times 0.055)$$
$$= 50 \sin 5.5\,\pi$$

The angle $5.5\,\pi$ is in radians and represents two complete rotations $(2 \times 2\pi)$ plus $3\pi/2$, which is the position of OP in Fig. 5.4 (d).

$$\therefore \sin 5.5\pi = -1$$
$$\therefore i = -50\text{A}$$

Since the amplitude of the function $50 \sin 100 \pi t$ is 50, this value of i is the maximum current in the negative direction.

5.5 Graph of $y = \sin(\theta + \alpha)$ where α is a constant

We shall draw the graph of $y = \sin(\theta + \pi/3)$ for values of θ from 0 to 2π radians, at intervals of $\pi/6$ radians, and compare its features with the basic sine curve, $y = \sin \theta$.

θ	0	$\dfrac{\pi}{6}$	$\dfrac{\pi}{3}$	$\dfrac{\pi}{2}$	$\dfrac{2\pi}{3}$	$\dfrac{5\pi}{6}$	π	$\dfrac{7\pi}{6}$	$\dfrac{4\pi}{3}$	$\dfrac{3\pi}{2}$	$\dfrac{5\pi}{3}$	$\dfrac{11\pi}{6}$	2π
$\left(\theta + \dfrac{\pi}{3}\right)$	$\dfrac{\pi}{3}$	$\dfrac{\pi}{2}$	$\dfrac{2\pi}{3}$	$\dfrac{5\pi}{6}$	π	$\dfrac{7\pi}{6}$	$\dfrac{4\pi}{3}$	$\dfrac{3\pi}{2}$	$\dfrac{5\pi}{3}$	$\dfrac{11\pi}{6}$	2π	$\dfrac{13\pi}{6}$	$\dfrac{7\pi}{3}$
$\sin\left(\theta + \dfrac{\pi}{3}\right)$	0·87	1	0·87	0·5	0	−0·5	−0·87	−1	−0·87	−0·5	0	0·5	0·87

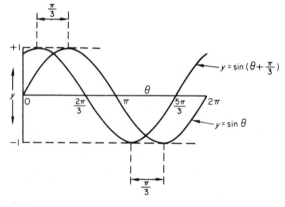

Fig. 5.11

On the graph of $y = \sin(\theta + \pi/3)$, the following important comparisons are made with the graph of $y = \sin \theta$.

(a) the two graphs have the same shape,

(b) their periods are equal, i.e., 2π radians,

(c) their amplitudes are equal, i.e., 1,

(d) the graph of $\sin(\theta + \pi/3)$ reaches its maximum, zero, and minimum values, $\pi/3$ radians ahead of $\sin \theta$; it is said to 'lead' $\sin \theta$ by $\pi/3$ at all points. Similarly, the graph of $y = \sin(\theta - \pi/3)$ would 'lag' (behind) $\sin \theta$ by $\pi/3$. In general, $\sin(\theta + \alpha)$ is said to have a 'phase difference of angle α' when compared with $\sin \theta$.

Any quantity which is alternating produces a repeating cycle of values. If these values when plotted, produce the graph of a sine curve, then the quantity is said to vary sinusoidally, and the graph is referred to as a wave. Current, voltage, and e.m.f. may each vary sinusoidally and it is this type of variation which is important in the study of a.c.

An alternating current can be expressed by

$$i = I_m \sin \omega t \text{ or } i = I_m \sin 2\pi ft$$

and an e.m.f. by

$$e = E_m \sin \omega t \quad \text{or} \quad e = E_m \sin 2\pi ft$$

where I_m, E_m, and ω are constants.

Note the convention of using a small letter i or e for an instantaneous value of an alternating quantity; I_m and E_m are the maximum values of current and e.m.f. Since the two functions, $I_m \sin \omega t$ and $E_m \sin \omega t$ have the same frequency, $\omega/2\pi$ or f Hz, then they can be represented on the same graph with appropriate scales of units for i and e; the same time scale would satisfy both functions. The maximum values of i and e would be reached when $t = \pi/2\omega$ sec, the minimum values when $t = 3\pi/2\omega$ sec; the two functions are said to be 'in phase'.

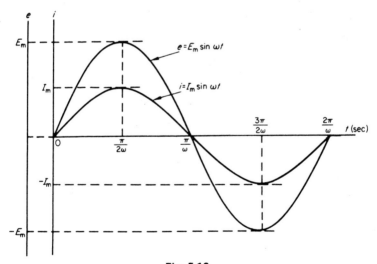

Fig. 5.12

Example 5.16. A sinusoidal current of maximum value 10A has a frequency of 40 Hz; at $t = 0$, the current is zero. Develop a trigonometrical expression for the value of the instantaneous current i at time t sec.

Let $i = R \sin 2\pi ft$; therefore

$$i = 10 \sin 2\pi \times 40 t$$
$$= 10 \sin 80 \pi t$$

Example 5.17. An e.m.f. which varies sinusoidally, has a maximum value of 100 V and a time period of 0·1 sec; at $t = 0$, e.m.f. $= 0$. Develop a trigonometrical expression for the instantaneous e.m.f. e at time t sec.

$$\text{Time period} = T = 0\cdot1 \text{ sec}$$
$$\therefore \text{Frequency} = 1/T = 10 \text{ Hz}$$
$$\therefore \omega = 2\pi f = 2\pi \times 10 = 20\pi \text{ rad/s}$$
$$\therefore e = 100 \sin 20 \pi t$$

Example 5.18. An alternating current has a frequency of 100 Hz. Its value at time $t = 0$ is 7·5 A and its maximum value is 15 A. Find an expression for the instantaneous value i at time t, assuming that it varies sinusoidally.

Frequency, $f = 100$ Hz,

$$\therefore \omega = 2\pi f = 2\pi \times 100 = 200 \pi \text{ rad/s}$$

Let $i = 15 \sin (200 \pi t + \phi)$
At $t = 0$ $\qquad\qquad\qquad i = 7\cdot5$

$$\therefore 7\cdot5 = 15 \sin \phi$$
$$\therefore 0\cdot5 = \sin \phi$$
$$\therefore \frac{\pi}{6} = \phi$$

considering only the smallest positive value of ϕ

$$\therefore i = 15 \sin \left(200 \pi t + \frac{\pi}{6} \right)$$

EXERCISE 5.2

1. Convert the following time periods in seconds into frequencies; state the units of your answer, correct to three significant figures.

(a) 0·02   (b) 0·004   (c) 0·05
(d) $\pi \times 10^{-3}$ (e) 10^{-5}

2. An armature rotates at the following angular velocities in rad/s; convert these into frequencies, stating the units of your answer correct to three significant figures.

(a) 500   (b) $2 \cdot 2 \times 10^2$ (c) 450
(d) $\pi \times 10^3$ (e) 10^4

3. The following velocities of rotation are given in rev/s; convert these into angular velocities stating the units of your answer, correct to three significant figures.

(a) 230   (b) 1500   (c) $10^4/3 \cdot 14$
(d) 1   (e) $1/2\pi$

4. The time periods in seconds of an alternating quantity are as follows:

(a) 0·002   (b) π (c) $5 \cdot 8 \times 10^{-2}$
(d) $3 \cdot 14 \times 10^{-3}$ (e) $1/f$

Assuming that the variation of the quantity can be represented by a line rotating at a constant angular velocity, convert these time periods into angular velocities. Give your answers correct to three significant figures, stating the units.

5. (a) State the values of (i) tan 143° 35', (ii) sin $(11\pi/18$ radians)
   (b) Evaluate $(100\pi t - 45°)$ when $t = 0 \cdot 01$ giving the answer in radians.
   (c) If $I = 70 \cdot 7 \sin (100\pi t + \pi/4)$, calculate the value of I when $t = 0 \cdot 01$.

   E.M.E.U.

6. The value of a current is given by $i = 60 \sin (300t - 0 \cdot 2)$. Calculate

   (a) i when $t = 0 \cdot 003$
   (b) the maximum value of i and the value of t when this first occurs.

   U.E.I.

7. If $i = 100 \sin (80\pi t - \pi/4)$ amp, where t is in sec:

   (a) determine the amplitude and period of the function
   (b) calculate the value of i when $t = 0$
   (c) calculate the smallest positive value of t when $i = 0$.

   Y.C. (part Qn.)

8. Evaluate

    (a) sin 230°

    (b) $V \sin(\omega t + \phi)$ where $V = 300$ volt, $\omega = 100\pi$ rad/s, $t = 0.14$ sec, $\phi = 0.2$ radians.

Y.C. (part Qn.)

9. Draw a graph of $v = 4 \sin(2\pi t - \pi/3)$ by plotting points between $t = 0$ and $t = 1$ at intervals of 0·1 of a second. From the graph estimate the values of t when $v = 2$.

Y.C.

10. An alternating current is represented by the equation $i = 10 \sin \omega t$ amp, where $\omega = 100\pi$ and t is time in sec. Plot a graph of i against t, with t horizontal, from $t = 0$ to $t = 0.02$ sec. Use the graph to find:

    (a) the times when $i = 8.66$A (positive)
    (b) the current when $t = 0.015$ sec
    (c) the greatest positive value of i.

U.L.C.I.

11. The current in an a.c. circuit at any time t sec is given by $i = 50 \sin(200\pi t - 0.1)$

    (a) Find the value of i when $t = 0$ and $t = 0.02$ sec
    (b) Find the first value of t when $i = 0$
    (c) Sketch a graph of the function for one period, marking the maximum and minimum values of i and the values of t where the curve cuts the t-axis.

U.E.I. (part Qn.)

12. An alternating voltage is given by $v = 230 \sin(100\pi t - 0.3)$.

    (a) State the amplitude, period, and frequency of the oscillation.
    (b) Calculate the first positive value of t for which $v = 100$.

C.G.L.I. E.T. (part Qn.)

13. A current i (amp) is defined by $i = 200 \sin(300\pi t - 0.04)$, where t is in sec.

    (a) State the amplitude, period, and frequency of the current.
    (b) Calculate the value of i when $t = 0.01$.
    (c) On the same axes, draw sketch graphs to show the difference between

$$i = 200 \sin 300\pi t$$
$$i = 200 \sin(300\pi t - 0.04)$$
and $$i = 200 \sin(300\pi t + 0.04)$$

C.G.L.I. E.T. (part Qn.)

14. An alternating current i amp in a circuit at any time t sec is given by $i = 40 \sin (200 \pi t + 0.1)$, the angle being measured in radians. Find

   (a) the value of i when $t = 0$ and when $t = 0.01$ sec,
   (b) one value of t for which $i = 0$ and $i = 40$.

U.L.C.I.

15. The instantaneous value of an electric current, i amp, at any time t sec is given by the expression, $i = 20 \cos (100 \pi t + \pi/4)$ where the angle is measured in radians. Find

   (a) the value of i when $t = 0$ and when $t = 0.01$ sec,
   (b) one value of t for which $i = 0$,
   (c) one value of t for which $i = 10$ amp.

U.L.C.I.

16. Draw on the same diagram, complete cycles of an alternating voltage of maximum value 100 V and an alternating current of maximum value 20 A, given that the current lags 60° behind the voltage; assume that current and voltage vary sinusoidally with the same frequency. From your diagram, read,

   (a) the current when the voltage is a maximum,
   (b) the voltage when the current is a maximum.

17. An alternating current of sinusoidal character reaches its maximum positive value 0.01 sec before the succeeding maximum negative value. Calculate the frequency and write down a suitable function for i, given that its maximum value is 20 A and at $t = 0$, $i = 10$ A.

18. An alternating current is given by $i = 48.5 \sin 350\, t$. Calculate,

   (a) the frequency
   (b) the time in seconds when the current first reaches 20 A.

19. An alternating current in a circuit containing a reactance is given by $i = 50 \sin 100 \pi t$. The voltage across the reactance is given by $v = 100 \sin (100 \pi t + \pi/2)$. State

   (a) the maximum values of current and voltage,
   (b) the phase angle between current and voltage. In the expression of your answer, use the term 'lead' or 'lag'.

20. Write down an expression for the instantaneous value v of a sinusoidal alternating voltage of maximum value V_m frequency f and phase angle ϕ, leading.

After 0·01 sec the voltage is 50% of maximum and after 0·012 sec the voltage is 86·6% of maximum. Calculate the values of f and ϕ.

5.6   Maximum, average, and root mean square values

Sections 5.4 and 5.5 have shown a very close relationship between the graph of $\sin \theta$ and the variation of an alternating current. If the behaviour of the current can be described mathematically by a sine function, we say it varies sinusoidally; this is just one of its characteristics. An isolated quality, however, is insufficient to identify and compare two or more examples of the same type of quantity and we have become a little more informed about the sine wave by understanding what is meant by the period, frequency, and phase angle. Whilst these measurements are very useful, they do not supply the answer to the most important consideration, namely, what is the strength of the current? The term 'strength' has been chosen deliberately in order not to assume the answer and to encourage the further question, 'by what measurement must we judge the strength of a current, maximum or average?' Each of these dimensions can be shown to have a useful application and yet not be sufficient separately.

(a) *Maximum*

Figures 5.13(a) and 5.13(b) show different types of waveform in two circuits.

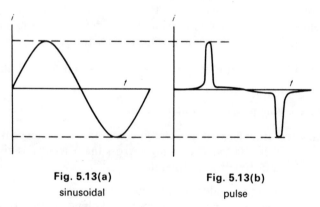

Fig. 5.13(a)
sinusoidal

Fig. 5.13(b)
pulse

Although the maximum values of current are the same, it is clear that the current in Fig. 5.13(b), maintaining its maximum value over a very short interval of time, could not provide an equally useful heating effect as the current in Fig. 5.13(a).

(b) *Average*

Figures 5.14(a) and 5.14(b) show the effect of comparing average values.

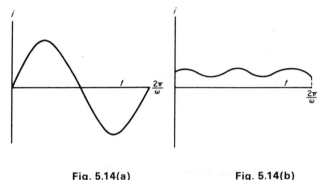

Fig. 5.14(a)
sinusoidal

Fig. 5.14(b)
alternating but remaining positive

The average value of Fig. 5.14(a) is zero for the time period $2\pi/\omega$ sec; the average value of Fig. 5.14(b) over the same time interval, is some positive value not far short of its maximum value, yet the heating effect of Fig. 5.14(a) could be greater than that of Fig. 5.14(b).

Since it is the alternately varying sign of the current in Fig. 5.14(a) which produces the apparently useless zero average, we must determine the equivalent direct current; the equivalence is based on a measurement of power. The value of this equivalent direct current is called the 'effective value' of the alternating current, or 'root mean square' (r.m.s.) value.

The instantaneous power produced in a non-inductive resistance $R\Omega$ by an alternating current, $i = I_m \sin \omega t$, is Ri^2 watts or $RI_m^2 \sin^2 \omega t$.

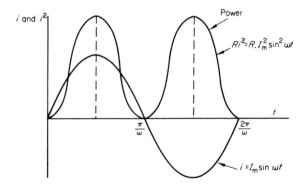

Fig. 5.15

Figure 5.15 shows the effect of drawing the graph of power, Ri^2; the negative part of the current $i = I_m \sin \omega t$ between $t = \pi/\omega$ and $t = 2\pi/\omega$ sec is now shown as a positive cycle of power, equal to the power cycle from 0 to π/ω sec. Therefore,

$$\binom{\text{Average power effect of}}{\text{the alternating current}} = \text{average of } Ri^2$$
$$= R \text{ (which is a constant)}$$
$$\times \text{ average value of } i^2 \text{ over one cycle}$$

If I is the direct current whose power effect is the same as the average power effect of the alternating current, then

$$RI^2 = R \times (\text{average value of } i^2)$$
$$\therefore I^2 = (\text{average value of } i^2)$$
$$\therefore I = \sqrt{(\text{average value of } i^2)}$$

The word 'mean' is used in place of average, hence

$$I = \sqrt{(\text{mean value of } i^2)}$$

giving rise to the term, 'root mean square' value.

Determination of average and r.m.s. values

In comparing (a) and (b) of Fig. 5.13, the impression is gained that (a) represents a larger strength of current than (b) because the near-maximum values persist over a longer interval of time than those of (b). This is equivalent to saying that we must take into account height *and* width of the graph; hence area under the graph is the important factor.

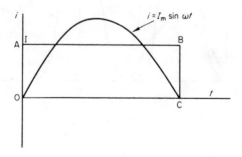

Fig. 5.16

The rectangle OABC has the same area as the half-cycle of the wave. The height, I amp, of the rectangle, is thus the equivalent direct current whose value is the average value of i.

Depending on the accuracy required, this value may be found directly by the mid-ordinate rule, or in more difficult examples, from the relation,

$$\text{Height of rectangle} = \frac{\text{area}}{\text{length of base}}$$

the area then being found by more accurate methods such as Simpson's rule or by calculus.

5.7 Mid-ordinate rule to find the average height of a curve

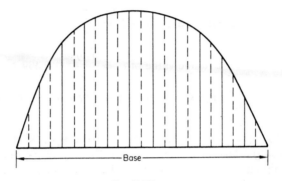

Fig. 5.17

Divide the base into a number of parts of equal width by lines drawn at right-angles to the base and reaching the curve. At the mid-point of each of these widths, draw and measure vertical lines to meet the curve; these are called 'mid-ordinates'. The average length of these lines is then the average height of the curve.

If the curve used is $i = I_m \sin \omega t$, the average height is the average value of current. If the curve used is $i^2 = I_m^2 \sin^2 \omega t$, the square root of the average height will be the r.m.s. value of the current. In these two cases, it is not necessary to draw the curve and measure mid-ordinates, the values being obtainable from tables of sines. We can consider a half wave of the graph $i = \sin \theta$ from $0°$ to $180°$, with the base of the graph divided into nine equal widths at $\theta = 0°, 20°, 40°$, etc. The values of $\sin \theta$ and $\sin^2 \theta$ at $10°, 30°, 50°$, etc., are tabulated overleaf.

Mid-ordinate (degrees)	Height (i)	(Height)^2 (i^2)
10	0·17	0·029
30	0·50	0·25
50	0·77	0·59
70	0·94	0·88
90	1·00	1·00
110	0·94	0·88
130	0·77	0·59
150	0·50	0·25
170	0·17	0·029
	Sum 5·76	4·498

$$\therefore \text{ average value of } i, I_{av} = \frac{5·76}{9} = 0·64 \text{ A}$$

$$\therefore \text{ average value of } i^2 = \frac{4·498}{9} = 0·499 \text{ A}$$

$$\therefore \text{ r.m.s. value of } i, I = \sqrt{0·499} = 0·706 \text{ A}$$

Greater accuracy would be obtained if the base of the curve were divided into a larger number of parts; the mid-ordinate rule is, however, only an approximate method. The theoretical value of average and r.m.s. values of an alternating current which varies sinusoidally, are shown below.

If $i = \sin \theta$, then average value of $i = 0·637$ A and r.m.s. value of $i = 0·707$ A. These values are always related to the maximum value of current, so that, if $i = I_m \sin \theta$, then $I_{av} = 0·637 I_m$ and $I = 0·707 I_m$.

The proofs of these calculations, which will be given in Vol. 3, will show that,

$$I_{av} = \frac{2}{\pi} I_m$$

$$I = \frac{1}{\sqrt{2}} I_m$$

Note. In the study of alternating current, the following abbreviations of terms has been adopted

$$i = \text{instantaneous value}$$
$$I_m = \text{maximum value}$$
$$I_{av} = \text{average value}$$
$$I = \text{r.m.s. value}$$

Relations between maximum, average, and r.m.s. values

There are two important ratios which give a further indication of the type of wave which represents any alternating quantity.

(a)
$$\text{Form factor} = \frac{\text{r.m.s. value}}{\text{average value}}$$

For a sine wave,

$$\text{Form factor} = \frac{0.707 I_m}{0.637 I_m} = 1.11$$

For a rectangular wave the graph of the current shown in Fig. 5.18

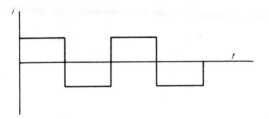

Fig. 5.18

satisfies the conditions of an alternating quantity, in that it passes through a complete cycle of values which are then repeated; the size of the current is constant, only the direction varies. Its maximum, average, and r.m.s. values are equal. Hence,

$$\text{Form factor} = \frac{\text{r.m.s. value}}{\text{average value}} = 1$$

Comparing this value with that of a sine wave, 1.11, it can be seen that the form factor is an indication of the shape of the wave; if the value is less than 1.11, the wave is usually flat-topped; if greater than 1.11, the wave is a 'peaky' wave.

(b)
$$\text{Crest factor} = \frac{\text{maximum value}}{\text{r.m.s. value}}$$

For a sine wave,

$$\text{Crest factor} = \frac{I_m}{0.707 I_m} = 1.414$$

From a knowledge of r.m.s. value and crest factor, the maximum value of current or voltage can be calculated and the circuit constructed to sustain these maximum values.

5.8 Simpson's rule to find areas

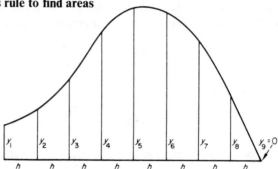

Fig. 5.19

The base line is divided into an even number of strips of equal width, and ordinates erected at these points are measured. The area under the curve is given by:

Area $= \dfrac{h}{3}$ [sum of first + last ordinate + 4 times the sum of the even ordinates + twice the sum of the odd ordinates, excluding the first and last]

where h is the width of each strip.

Hence, in Fig. 5.19,

$$\text{Area} = \frac{h}{3}[y_1 + y_9 + 4(y_2 + y_4 + y_6 + y_8) + 2(y_3 + y_5 + y_7)]$$

Example 5.19. The waveform of an alternating current has the shape of an isosceles triangle of maximum height 12 A. Calculate (a) the

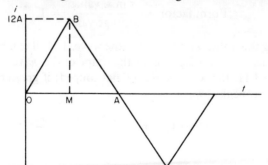

Fig. 5.20

average value and (b) the r.m.s. value of the current, and the form and crest factors of the wave.

(a) Average value

    (i) Using one half-cycle, the triangle OBA, we are required to find the height of a rectangle on a base of length OA whose area is equal to the area of the triangle OBA.

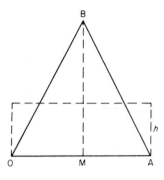

Fig. 5.20(a)

$$OA \times h = \frac{OA \times 12}{2}$$

$$\therefore h = 6$$

that is, average value of i, $I_{av} = 6A$

    (ii) By mid-ordinate rule

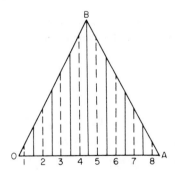

Fig. 5.20(b)

The base of the triangle is divided into eight parts of equal width and ordinates erected at these points. The mid-ordinates are drawn in each strip and measured; the results are shown below.

Mid-ordinate number	i	i^2
1	1·5	2·25
2	4·5	20·25
3	7·5	56·25
4	10·5	110·25
5	10·5	110·25
6	7·5	56·25
7	4·5	20·25
8	1·5	2·25

Number of ordinates = 8   Sum = 48   Sum = 378

$$\therefore \text{ average value of } i, I_{av} = \frac{48}{8} = 6A$$

(b) R.M.S. value

(i) By mid-ordinate rule, using the values of the table above:

$$\therefore \text{ Average value of } i^2 = \frac{378}{8} = 47 \cdot 25$$

$$\therefore \text{ r.m.s. value } = I = \sqrt{47 \cdot 25} = 6 \cdot 874 \text{ A}$$

(ii) By Simpson's rule
In Fig. 5.20(b), we use the (length)^2 of the ordinates to find an area; the length of the base is assumed to be 8 units, hence $h = 1$.

$$\begin{aligned}
\text{Area} &= \tfrac{1}{3}[0 + 0 + 4(3^2 + 9^2 + 9^2 + 3^2) \\
&\qquad\qquad\qquad + 2(6^2 + 12^2 + 6^2)] \\
&= \tfrac{1}{3}[4(9 + 81 + 81 + 9) + 2(36 + 144 + 36)] \\
&= \tfrac{1}{3}(4 \times 180 + 2 \times 216) \\
&= \tfrac{1}{3}(720 + 432) \\
&= \tfrac{1}{3} \times 1152 \\
&= 384
\end{aligned}$$

$$\therefore \text{ average of (lengths)}^2 = \frac{384}{8} = 48$$

$$\therefore \text{ r.m.s. value} = \sqrt{\text{average of (lengths)}^2}$$

$$= \sqrt{48}$$

$$\therefore I = 6\cdot928 \text{ A}$$

Note. (a) The r.m.s. value, $\sqrt{48}$, is accurate by this method.

(b) The first and last ordinates in Fig. 5.20(b) are each zero; they must be counted as ordinates.

(c) $I = \sqrt{48} = \sqrt{\dfrac{12^2}{3}} = \sqrt{\dfrac{(\text{maximum height})^2}{3}}$

$$I = \frac{\text{maximum current}}{\sqrt{3}}$$

It can be shown that this is true for any triangle.

Example 5.20. An alternating current has the following values over a half-wave.

Time (sec)	0	0·005	0·0075	0·010
Current (A)	0	12	10	0

Assuming the current increases or decreases uniformly between these observations, plot a graph of the current over the half-wave and calculate the r.m.s. and average values of the current.

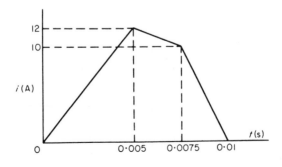

Fig. 5.21

(a) Average value

$$\text{Area} = \frac{12 \times 0.005}{2} + \frac{(10 + 12)}{2} \times 0.0025 + \frac{10 \times 0.0025}{2}$$

$$= 0.03 + 0.0275 + 0.0125$$

$$= 0.07$$

$$\text{Average height} = \frac{\text{area}}{\text{length of base}}$$

$$\therefore I = \frac{0.07}{0.01} = 7 \text{ A}$$

(b) R.M.S. value

It has been shown in Example 5.19 that the r.m.s. value of i for a tri-angular shape of wave is given by maximum current/$\sqrt{3}$. This value can be used for the first and last areas of the present example providing that we add together the energy represented by each area. We suppose that the current passes through a resistance of 1Ω producing RI^2t joules, where $R = 1$.

Hence, energy in first triangular area

$$= \frac{12^2}{3} \times 0.005 \text{ joules}$$

and energy in last triangular area

$$= \frac{10^2}{3} \times 0.0025 \text{ joules}$$

Trapezoidal area of Fig. 5.21

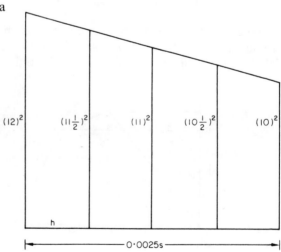

$(12)^2 \qquad (11\frac{1}{2})^2 \qquad (11)^2 \qquad (10\frac{1}{2})^2 \qquad (10)^2$

h

Fig. 5.21(a)

0.0025s

The ordinates are shown as i^2 since we are calculating I^2.

Applying Simpson's rule to the area of the trapezium:

$$\text{Area} = \frac{0 \cdot 000625}{3}\left[12^2 + 10^2 + 4(11 \cdot 5^2 + 10 \cdot 5^2) + 2(11^2)\right]$$

$$= \frac{0 \cdot 000625}{3}\left[144 + 100 + 4\left(\frac{529}{4} + \frac{441}{4}\right) + 242\right]$$

$$= \frac{0 \cdot 000625}{3}[244 + 529 + 441 + 242]$$

$$= \frac{0 \cdot 000625}{3}(1456)$$

This area represents the energy in joules.

$$\therefore \text{Total energy} = \frac{12^2}{3} \times 0 \cdot 005 + \frac{10^2}{3} \times 0 \cdot 0025$$

$$+ \frac{0 \cdot 000625}{3} \times 1456$$

$$= 48 \times 0 \cdot 005 + \frac{0 \cdot 25}{3} + 0 \cdot 3033$$

$$= 0 \cdot 240 + 0 \cdot 0833 + 0 \cdot 3033$$

$$= 0 \cdot 6266 \text{ joules}$$

$$\text{Average value of } i^2 = \frac{\text{energy}}{\text{time}} = \frac{0 \cdot 6266}{0 \cdot 01}$$

$$= 62 \cdot 66 \text{ (A)}^2 \text{ since } R = 1\Omega$$

$$\therefore \text{ r.m.s. value of } i = \sqrt{62 \cdot 66} = 7 \cdot 916 \text{ A}$$

EXERCISE 5.3

1. A sinusoidal alternating current has a maximum value of 4 A. Draw the graph of the current function over half a cycle and from it obtain the average and r.m.s. values of the current.

2. A sinusoidal alternating current of maximum value 50 A increases from zero to 25 A in $\frac{1}{600}$ sec. Calculate the phase angle in radians through which the current has passed and find also its frequency. Determine the value of the current after $\frac{1}{100}$ sec.

3. Draw the curve representing a half-wave of the alternating voltage given by $v = 10 \sin 2\pi ft$ given that $f = 50$. Use the mid-ordinate rule to find the average and root mean square values of voltage.

4. The values of an alternating current over a half-cycle are tabulated below.

Angle (rad.)	0	$\pi/8$	$\pi/4$	$3\pi/8$	$\pi/2$	$5\pi/8$	$3\pi/4$	$7\pi/8$	π
Current (A)	0	5	10	15	20	15	10	5	0

Draw the graph represented by these values, joining the points by straight lines. Use the graph to find the average value of the current and find the r.m.s. value of the current using Simpson's rule.

5. The period of an alternating voltage is $0·02$ sec. From $t = 0$ to $t = 0·0025$ sec the voltage rises uniformly from 0 V to 10 V; from $t = 0·0025$ sec to $t = 0·005$ sec it rises uniformly to 30 V and from $t = 0·005$ sec to $t = 0·01$ sec falls uniformly to zero. Draw a graph representing these variations and from it calculate the average and r.m.s. values of voltage over the half period.

6. An alternating current has a rectangular wave form with a period of 4 sec. During the first second, the current is a constant 5 A, and during the next second, its value is a constant 10 A. If the negative half-cycle is symmetrical find the average and root mean square values of current over a half-cycle: calculate also the form factor.

7. The form factor of a sinusoidal waveform of voltage, is $1·11$. If the average value of voltage is 100 V, calculate the r.m.s. value.

8. The crest factor for a sine wave representing an alternating current is $1·414$. If the r.m.s. value of the current is 50 A, calculate the maximum value of the current.

9. The insulation of a machine is made to withstand 550 V, direct current. Calculate the r.m.s. value of the greatest alternating voltage which can be applied to the machine, assuming a sinusoidal waveform.

5.9   Vectors

In §5.4 it was shown that a sine wave could be produced by a radius of a circle rotating at a constant angular velocity, ω rad/s.

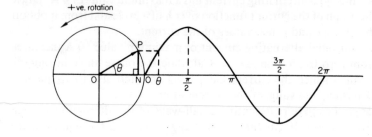

Fig. 5.22

In each position of the rotating radius OP, at angle θ, the perpendicular PN represented the magnitude, (i.e., the size), of the alternating current at the phase angle position θ on the sine wave. The value of i is completely determined by the length and position of OP. This combination of magnitude and direction, expressed in one line of a diagram, gives the name 'vector' to that line. OP is a rotating vector, the arrow head indicating the end of the line which rotates, the length of OP, drawn to some scale, representing the magnitude of current or voltage: the particular magnitude may be i the instantaneous value, I_m the maximum value, or I the r.m.s. value. The shape of the diagram would be unaltered and the relative positions of the vectors would remain the same. It is accepted practice to print vector quantities in bold type. thus,

It is important to remember that when alternating currents and voltages are represented by rotating vectors, it is assumed that their waveforms are sinusoidal.

Since the graph of $\cos \theta$ is the same shape as that of $\sin \theta$. differing only in position, a cosine function can be considered as sinusoidal if allowance is made for the phase angle lead of cosine; this has been shown graphically to be $90°$; a short proof of this is set out below.

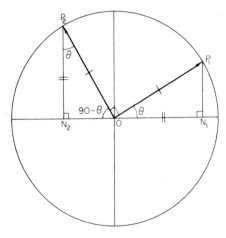

Fig. 5.23

Let a rotating vector OP turn through an angle θ to position OP_1. complete triangle OP_1N_1. Let the vector move through an additional angle of $90°$ to OP_2; complete the triangle OP_2N_2.

Hence
$$\angle N_1OP_2 = 90° + \theta$$
$$\therefore \ \angle P_2ON_2 = 90° - \theta \quad \text{and} \quad \angle OP_2N_2 = \theta$$

Hence $\triangle OP_1N_1$ and $\triangle OP_2N_2$ are congruent, having two angles and a corresponding side, equal.

$$\therefore \ ON_1 = P_2N_2 \quad \text{and} \quad OP_1 = OP_2$$

From $\triangle OP_1N_1$,

$$\cos \theta = ON_1/OP_1 = P_2N_2/OP_2$$
$$= \sin (90° - \theta)$$
$$= \sin (90° + \theta)$$
$$\therefore \cos \theta = \sin (90° + \theta)$$

or
$$\cos \theta = \sin (\theta + 90°)$$

Hence $\cos \theta$ leads $\sin \theta$ by 90°. If then a vector is given as a cosine function, it can be added or subtracted with other vectors in sine form by re-writing as $\sin (\theta + 90°)$.

Addition of alternating currents or voltages; vectorial method

Example 5.21. If $i_1 = 8 \sin \theta$ and $i_2 = 4 \sin (\theta + \pi/4)$, find the resultant current represented by $i_1 + i_2$.

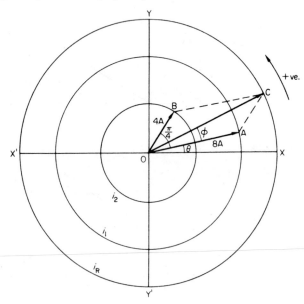

Fig. 5.24

The vectors **OA** and **OB** are drawn to scale to represent maximum values of current, 8 A and 4 A respectively. Current i_2 leads i_1 by a phase angle difference of $\pi/4$, hence $\angle$ AOB is constructed equal to 45° with **OB** in the leading position. The parallelogram OACB is completed and **OC** drawn.

If the student will now imagine OACB to be a rigid framework, pivoted at O and rotating in the positive direction, **OA** will describe circle i_1, **OB** circle i_2, and **OC** circle i_R (resultant); these circles can be considered as 'vectorial circles of current'. The position shown in Fig. 5.24 is for any phase angle θ of i_1. The maximum positive, zero, and maximum negative values of current will occur as each of the vectors **OA**, **OB**, and **OC** passes OY, OX', and OY' respectively. The length of **OC**, measured to the same scale as **OA** and **OB**, gives the maximum value of the resultant current, I_R; the angle ϕ is the phase angle by which i_R leads i_1.

Hence

$$i_R = I_R \sin (\theta + \phi)$$
$$\therefore \ i_R = 11 \cdot 2 \sin (\theta + 0 \cdot 25)$$

from the dimensions of Fig. 5.24.

An instantaneous value of i_R at any phase angle position will be represented on the figure by the length of a perpendicular from C to XOX'.

Subtraction of alternating currents or voltages

Example 5.22. Two alternating voltages are given by $v_1 = 20 \sin \omega t$ and $v_2 = 10 \sin (\omega t + \pi/3)$. Find by a vectorial method an expression to show $v_1 - v_2$.

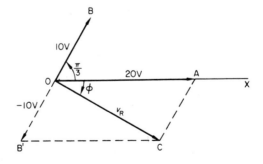

Fig. 5.25

Note. (a) For convenience, **OA** has been drawn along OX, i.e., for $t = 0$.
(b) **OB** is drawn to represent 10 V, leading **OA** by $\pi/3$ radians, but is
produced backwards an equal length to **OB'**, because we are finding
an expression for $v_1 - v_2$; this can be considered as the addition of
v_1 and $(-v_2)$.

The length of the resultant **OC**, the diagonal of the parallelogram
OACB', and the angle ϕ are measured. Hence,

$$v_1 - v_2 = v_R = OC \sin(\omega t - \phi)$$

From Fig. 5.25,

$$v_R = 17{\cdot}3 \sin(\omega t - 0{\cdot}52)$$

The resultant voltage v_R lags behind the voltage v_1 by a phase angle of
ϕ radians.

Example 5.23. Figures 5.26(a) and 5.26(b) below, show, without ex-
planation, the same vectorial method applied, when one alternating
quantity is lagging by an angle $\pi/6$ radians.

Let $i_1 = 15 \sin \omega t$ and let $i_2 = 5 \sin(\omega t - \pi/6)$.

(a) Find an expression for $i_1 + i_2$

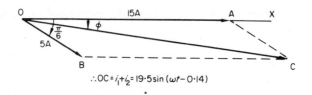

$$\therefore OC = i_1 + i_2 = 19{\cdot}5 \sin(\omega t - 0{\cdot}14)$$

Fig. 5.26(a)

(b) Find an expression for $i_1 - i_2$

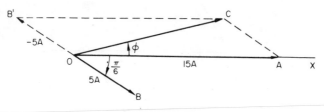

$$\therefore OC = i_1 - i_2 = 11 \sin(\omega t + 0{\cdot}23)$$

Fig. 5.26(b)

Addition of vectors; graphical method

Any point on a sine wave measures the magnitude of an alternating quantity at a particular position indicated by a phase angle θ; the graph of the alternating quantity is thus another form of vector. The addition of two such graphs should reach the same result as the method of Example 5.21.

Example 5.24. Draw the graphs of $i_1 = 8 \sin \theta$ and $i_2 = 4 \sin (\theta + \pi/4)$ on the same scale and axes, for values of θ from 0 to 2π radians. By the addition of ordinates, draw the graph of $i_1 + i_2$ and write down an expression for the resultant current, i_R.

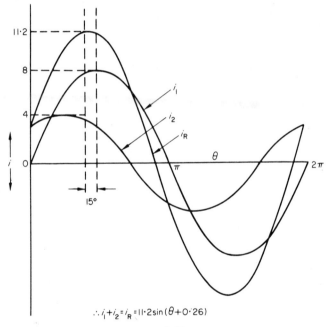

$$\therefore i_1 + i_2 = i_R = 11.2 \sin (\theta + 0.26)$$

Fig. 5.27

Addition of vectors: method of calculation

The following method, applied to the functions of Example 5.21, is more accurate than by drawing.

Example 5.25. If $i_1 = 8 \sin \theta$ and $i_2 = 4 \sin (\theta + \pi/4)$, find, by calculation, an expression for the resultant current, $i_1 + i_2$.

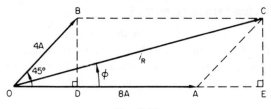

Fig. 5.28

Horizontal component of i_1 = OA = 8 A

Horizontal component of i_2 = OD = 4 cos 45° = AE

Total   Horizontal component of i_R = OE = OA + AE

$$= (8 + 4 \cos 45°) \text{ A}$$

Vertical component of i_1 = zero

Vertical component of i_2 = DB = 4 sin 45° = EC

Total   Vertical component of i_R = EC = (4 sin 45°) A

In △OEC,

$$OC^2 = OE^2 + EC^2 \quad \text{(Pythagoras' Theorem)}$$

$$\therefore OC^2 = (8 + 4 \cos 45°)^2 + (4 \sin 45°)^2$$

$$= \left(8 + 4\frac{1}{\sqrt{2}}\right)^2 + \left(4\frac{1}{\sqrt{2}}\right)^2$$

$$= \left(\frac{8\sqrt{2} + 4}{\sqrt{2}}\right)^2 + \left(\frac{4}{\sqrt{2}}\right)^2$$

$$= \frac{64 \times 2 + 16 + 2 \times 8\sqrt{2} \times 4}{2} + \frac{16}{2}$$

$$= \frac{128 + 16 + 64\sqrt{2}}{2} + 8$$

$$= 64 + 8 + 32\sqrt{2} + 8$$

$$= 80 + 32\sqrt{2}$$

$$= 80 + 45 \cdot 2$$

$$= 125 \cdot 2$$

$$\therefore OC = \sqrt{125 \cdot 2} = 11 \cdot 2 \text{ A}$$

and $$\tan \phi = \frac{CE}{OE} = \frac{4 \sin 45°}{8 + 4 \cos 45°}$$

$$\therefore \phi = 14·6° = 0·255 \text{ radians (leading)}$$

Hence
$$i_R = 11·2 \sin (\theta + 0·255)$$

Vectorial notation

A vector quantity is often given in an abbreviated form showing magnitude in normal size type and direction as a suffix to the magnitude.

Example 5.26. Using a scale of 1 cm representing 10 units, obtain the vector sum of $34·5_0$, $13·5_{-37°}$, and $8·0_{53°}$. E.M.E.U. (part Qn.)

The $0°$ direction is OX, positive angles being measured anticlockwise from OX and negative angles clockwise.

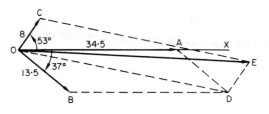

Fig. 5.29

Draw **OA** 3·45 cm along OX.
Draw **OB** 1·35 cm at $37°$ lagging.
Draw **OC** 0·8 cm at $53°$ leading.
Complete parallelogram OADB and join **OD**; this is the resultant of **OA** and **OB**.
Complete the parallelogram OCED and join **OE**.
Measure the length of **OE** and the angle AOE.
Hence the resultant of the three vectors is $50_{-2°}$.

Alternative method

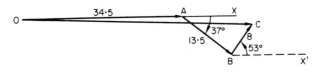

Fig. 5.30

Draw **OA** 3·45 cm along OX.

At A draw **AB** 1·35 cm at an angle of $-37°$ to OX.

At B draw **BC** 0·8 cm at an angle of $+53°$ to BX′.

The resultant is **OC**, of magnitude 50 and direction $-2°$; i.e., $50_{-2°}$.

EXERCISE 5.4

Find the vectorial sum of the alternating quantities in questions 1 to 4.

1. $i_1 = 4 \sin \omega t$　and　$i_2 = 2 \sin (\omega t + \pi/3)$.
2. $v_1 = 10 \sin (\omega t - \pi/6)$　and　$v_2 = 5 \sin \omega t$.
3. $e_1 = 50 \sin (\theta - \pi/3)$　and　$e_2 = 30 \sin (\theta + \pi/6)$.
4. $i_1 = 10 \sin 2\pi f t$　and　$i_2 = 50 \sin (2\pi f t + \pi/4)$.

Find the vectorial difference, $i_1 - i_2$, etc., between the following pairs of alternating quantities in questions 5 to 8.

5. $i_1 = 6 \sin 2\pi f t$　and　$i_2 = 3 \sin (2\pi f t + 0·5)$.
6. $e_1 = 20 \sin \omega t$　and　$e_2 = 30 \sin (\omega t + \pi/6)$.
7. $v_1 = 15 \sin (\theta - \pi/3)$　and　$v_2 = 10 \sin \theta$.
8. $i_1 = 5\sqrt{2} \sin (\theta - \pi/4)$　and　$i_2 = 8\sqrt{3} \sin \theta$.
9. Find the vectorial sum of $12_{72°}$, $8_{54°}$, and $6_{30°}$.
10. Find the resultant of $5_{120°}$, $4_{150°}$, and $10_{45°}$.
11. Draw on the same scale and axes, the two graphs $i_1 = 10 \sin \theta$ and $i_2 = 5 \sin (\theta + 1·05)$ for values of θ from 0 to 2π radians. By adding ordinates, obtain the graph of $i_1 + i_2$ and write down a sinusoidal expression to represent this graph.
12. (a) On the same axes and with the same scales, plot the graphs of (i) $y = 2 \cos x$ and (ii) $y = \sin (x + 40°)$ between $x = 0$ and $x = 180°$, and hence solve the equation,

$$2 \cos x - \sin (x + 40°) = 0$$

　　(b) By adding ordinates, obtain the graph of $y = 2 \cos x + \sin (x + 40°)$ and from this graph obtain a solution of the equation,

$$2 \cos x + \sin (x + 40°) = 0$$
Y.C.

13. Plot the graphs of $i_1 = 50 \sin 100 \pi t$ and $i_2 = 120 \cos 100 \pi t$ between $t = 0$ and $t = 0·02$ at intervals of 0·001. By adding ordinates obtain the graph of $i_1 + i_2$ and using this final graph, express $i_1 + i_2$ in the form,

$$i_r = I_m \sin (100 \pi t + \phi)$$

giving your estimates of I_m and ϕ.
Y.C.

14. Explain how a sinusoidal waveform can be derived from a rotating radius vector. Using this method or otherwise, construct a curve representing one cycle of a sinusoidal alternating voltage having a periodic time of $\frac{1}{200}$ sec and amplitude of 10 V.

   On the same axes, construct a sinusoidal current waveform of the same frequency leading the voltage by a phase difference of 90° and having an amplitude of 1 A. Without calculating any component value, sketch a simple circuit that will produce this phase difference between current and voltage.   C.G.L.I. T.T.

15. From the information given in the figure, calculate (a) the length of AD, (b) the angle ϕ.

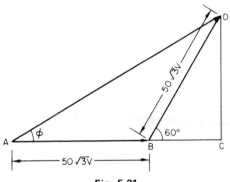

Fig. 5.31   E.M.E.U.

16. Add vectorially the following three voltages; $V_a = 100 \sin (\theta - 45°)$, $V_b = 50 \sin (\theta + 30°)$, and $V_c = 60 \cos \theta$. Give the value of the resultant voltage in the form, $V_R = V_M \sin (\theta \pm \alpha)$.
                                    E.M.E.U. (part Qn.)

17. In Fig. 5.32, **AB** and **BC** are vectors representing the alternating currents in two branches of a parallel circuit. The line **AC** is the resultant or total current. If **AB** is equivalent to 20 A, **BC** is equivalent to 15 A and ∠BCA is 30°, calculate the resultant current **AC** and the angle it makes with respect to **AB**.

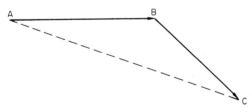

Fig. 5.32   U.L.C.I.

18. The current in a circuit is the resultant of the three currents i_1, i_2, and i_3. The magnitudes of i_1, i_2, and i_3 are 2, 4, and 5 respectively, and their directions are as shown in the diagram. Find the resultant current (a) by calculation, (b) by a scale drawing.

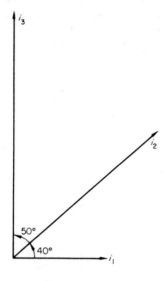

Fig. 5.33

U.E.I.

19. Find the magnitude and direction of the resultant of the three forces shown in the figure. What fourth force must be added to these three to give a system of forces in equilibrium?

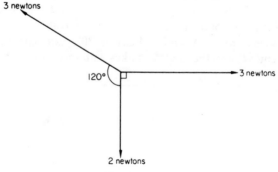

Fig. 5.34

C.G.L.I. T.T. (part Qn.)

20. (a) Evaluate (i) sin 230°, (ii) $V \sin (\omega t + \phi)$ where $V = 300$ volts, $\omega = 100 \pi$ rad/s, $t = 0.14$ sec, and $\phi = 0.2$ radians.

   (b) Figure 5.35 represents the voltages in a circuit involving a transformer. If $V_1 = 200$ V $RI = 8$ V, and $XI = 100$ V, calculate the value of V_2.

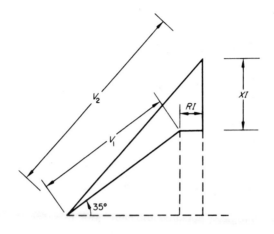

Fig. 5.35

Y.C.

6. Trigonometry

6.1 Solution of triangles; sine rule

In a right-angled triangle, it is possible to state the trigonometrical ratios, sine, cosine, and tangent, as ratios between pairs of particular sides of the triangle, opposite, adjacent, and hypotenuse. It is important to remember that the names of these sides refer only to right-angled triangles. However, an angle, say of 25°, occurring in a triangle which is not right-angled, will have the same values for its sine, cosine, and tangent as it would in a right-angled triangle, but they will not be represented completely by the ratios of two sides of the triangle.

Sine rule

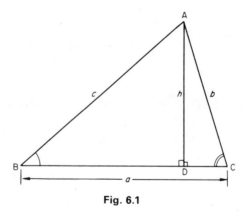

Fig. 6.1

In △ABC, which is not right-angled, a line AD is drawn from A perpendicular to BC; let this length be h. The lengths of the sides of △ABC are a, b, and c respectively, opposite angles A, B, and C. AD is a side common to the two right-angled triangles ABD and ADC.

In $\triangle$ABD, $\dfrac{h}{c} = \sin B$ In $\triangle$ADC, $\dfrac{h}{b} = \sin C$

$$\therefore h = c \sin B \qquad\qquad \therefore h = b \sin C$$

$$\therefore c \sin B = b \sin C$$

$$\therefore \frac{c}{\sin C} = \frac{b}{\sin B}$$

Similarly it can be shown that,

$$\frac{c}{\sin C} = \frac{a}{\sin A}$$

Hence,

$$\frac{a}{\sin A} = \frac{b}{\sin B} = \frac{c}{\sin C}$$

This is known as the Sine Rule.

Example 6.1. In $\triangle$ABC, $a = 5$, $\angle A = 40°$, and $\angle B = 70°$. Calculate the length of b.

$$\frac{b}{\sin B} = \frac{a}{\sin A}$$

$$\therefore b = \frac{a \sin B}{\sin A}$$

$$= \frac{5 \times \sin 70°}{\sin 40°} = \frac{5 \times 0{\cdot}9397}{0{\cdot}6428}$$

$$= 7{\cdot}31$$

Example 6.2. In $\triangle$CDE, $c = 10$, $d = 12$, and $\angle C = 50°$. Calculate the size of $\angle D$.

$$\frac{\sin D}{d} = \frac{\sin C}{c}$$

$$\therefore \sin D = \frac{d \sin C}{c}$$

$$= \frac{12 \times \sin 50°}{10} = \frac{12 \times 0{\cdot}7660}{10}$$

$$= 0{\cdot}9192$$

Since $\sin \theta = \sin(180° - \theta)$, then, from $\sin D = 0.9192$,

$$\angle D = 66° 49' \text{ or } 113° 11'$$

To determine whether each of these angles is a solution, we refer to the value of $\angle C$. Since $\angle C = 50°$, each of the values of $\angle D$ is possible.

Ambiguous solution

Where each of the values of an angle is possible, the solution is referred to as 'ambiguous', illustrated in Fig. 6.2, using the values of Example 6.2.

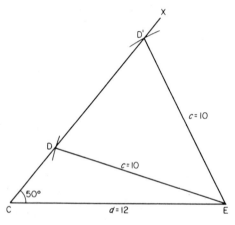

Fig. 6.2

The occurrence of the ambiguity can be seen if we consider the construction of $\triangle$ CDE.

Draw EC 12 units long and at C draw CX, making $\angle$ ECX $= 50°$. With centre E and radius 10 units, describe an arc to cut CX; this may occur at D or D'. Two triangles, CDE or CD'E are possible, where $\angle$ CDE is obtuse and $\angle$ CD'E is acute.

Comparing Examples 6.1 and 6.2, it should be noted that the ratios representing the sine rule have been applied in such a manner that the value to be calculated is in the numerator.

Example 6.3. Two angles of a triangle are 80° and 40°, Calculate the ratio of the sides opposite these angles.

Let $\angle A = 80°$ and $\angle B = 40°$

From $\dfrac{a}{\sin A} = \dfrac{b}{\sin B}$

$$a \sin B = b \sin A$$

$$\therefore \dfrac{a}{b} = \dfrac{\sin A}{\sin B}$$

$$= \dfrac{\sin 80°}{\sin 40°} = \dfrac{0·9848}{0·6428}$$

$$= \dfrac{1·53}{1}$$

The ratios of the sides of a triangle are determined by the sines of the angles opposite, not the angles themselves.

6.2 Cosine rule

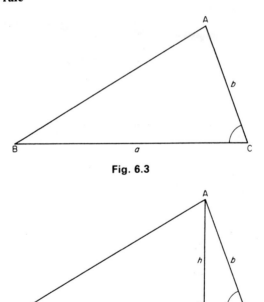

Fig. 6.3

Fig. 6.3(a)

The dimensions of the $\triangle ABC$ which are known, a, b, and C, fall into a recognizable pattern—two sides and the included angle. In these circumstances, the solution of the triangle depends on the use of the cosine rule, which is an extension of Pythagoras' theorem.

In Fig. 6.3(a), from $\triangle$ADB,

$$h^2 = AB^2 - (a - x)^2$$

and from $\triangle$ADC,

$$h^2 = b^2 - x^2$$
$$\therefore AB^2 - (a - x)^2 = b^2 - x^2$$
$$\therefore AB^2 = b^2 - x^2 + (a - x)^2$$
$$= b^2 - x^2 + a^2 - 2ax + x^2$$
$$= b^2 + a^2 - 2ax$$

In $\triangle$ ADC,

$$\frac{x}{b} = \cos C$$

$$\therefore x = b \cos C$$
$$\therefore AB^2 = a^2 + b^2 - 2\,ab \cos C$$
$$\therefore c^2 = a^2 + b^2 - 2ab \cos C$$

Similarly $\qquad a^2 = b^2 + c^2 - 2bc \cos A$

and $\qquad b^2 = a^2 + c^2 - 2ac \cos B$

The second power of each term is in keeping with Pythagoras' theorem.

Example 6.4. In $\triangle$EFG, EF = 5 cm, FG = 7 cm, and $\angle$ EFG = 40°. Calculate the length of EG.

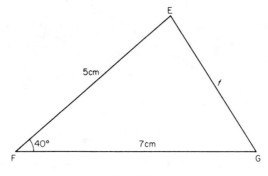

Fig. 6.4

By the cosine rule,

$$f^2 = 5^2 + 7^2 - 2 \times 5 \times 7 \cos 40°$$
$$= 25 + 49 - 70 \cos 40°$$
$$= 74 - 70 \, (0·7660)$$
$$= 74 - 53·62$$
$$= 20·38$$

$$\therefore f = \sqrt{20·38}$$
$$= 4·52 \text{ cm}$$

Example 6.5. In $\triangle PQR$, $PQ = 3$ cm, $QR = 6$ cm, and $\angle PQR = 130°$. Calculate the length of PR.

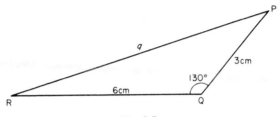

Fig. 6.5

Note that the given angle is obtuse and therefore its cosine will be negative.

By the cosine rule,

$$q^2 = 6^2 + 3^2 - 2 \times 6 \times 3 \cos 130°$$
$$= 36 + 9 - 36 \, (-\cos 50°)$$
$$= 45 + 36 \cos 50°$$
$$= 45 + 36 \, (0·6428)$$
$$= 45 + 23·14$$
$$= 68·14$$
$$\therefore q = 8·25 \text{ cm}$$

Cosine rule, given the lengths of three sides of a triangle

Example 6.6. In $\triangle ABC$, $a = 8$ cm, $b = 6$ cm, and $c = 12$ cm. Calculate the size of $\angle A$.

The original statement of the cosine rule which involves the angle A requires to be modified so that cos A becomes the subject.

$$a^2 = b^2 + c^2 - 2bc \cos A$$
$$\therefore 2bc \cos A = b^2 + c^2 - a^2$$
$$\therefore \cos A = \frac{b^2 + c^2 - a^2}{2bc}$$

Hence, in this case

$$\cos A = \frac{6^2 + 12^2 - 8^2}{2 \times 6 \times 12}$$
$$= \frac{36 + 144 - 64}{144}$$
$$= \frac{116}{144}$$

No.	log
116	2·0645
144	2·1584
	$\bar{1}$·9061

A = 36° 20′ (use log cosines)

Example 6.7. In $\triangle ABC$, $a = 2$ cm, $b = 4$ cm, and $c = 5$ cm. Calculate the size of the largest angle.

The largest angle will be opposite the longest side.

From $c^2 = a^2 + b^2 - 2ab \cos C$

$$2ab \cos C = a^2 + b^2 - c^2$$
$$\therefore \cos C = \frac{a^2 + b^2 - c^2}{2ab}$$

Hence, in this case

$$\cos C = \frac{2^2 + 4^2 - 5^2}{2 \times 2 \times 4}$$
$$= \frac{4 + 16 - 25}{16}$$
$$= -\frac{5}{16} = -0·3125$$

Note that cos C is negative, indicating that $\angle C$ is obtuse, its value being the supplement of the angle whose cosine, 0·3125, we read in the cosine tables.

$$\therefore \ \angle C \text{ is the supplement of } 71° \ 47'$$
$$\therefore \ \angle C = 180° - 71° \ 47'$$
$$= 108° \ 13'$$

The cosine rule does not lend itself easily to the use of logarithms, but generally requires to be used only once in any problem. Any further calculation of lengths and angles should follow the sine rule.

6.3 Area of a triangle; two sides and the included angle known

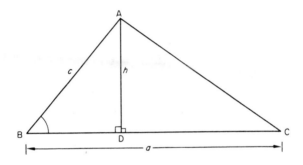

Fig. 6.6

$$\triangle ABC = \frac{\text{base} \times \text{height}}{2} = \frac{ah}{2}$$

In $\triangle ADB$,

$$\frac{h}{c} = \sin B, \qquad \therefore \ h = c \sin B$$

$$\therefore \ \triangle ABC = \frac{ac \sin B}{2} = \tfrac{1}{2}ac \sin B$$

Similarly it can be shown that,

$$\triangle ABC = \tfrac{1}{2}ab \sin C$$

or $$\triangle ABC = \tfrac{1}{2}bc \sin A$$

Example 6.8. A parallelogram ABCD has AB = 4 cm, BC = 2 cm, and ∠ABC = 50°. Calculate its area.

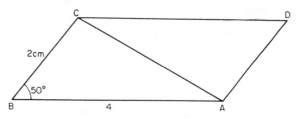

Fig. 6.7

The diagonal CA divides the area of the parallelogram into two equal triangles ABC and ACD.

$$\text{Area of } \triangle ABC = \tfrac{1}{2}ac \sin B$$
$$= \tfrac{1}{2} \times 2 \times 4 \times \sin 50°$$
$$= 4 \times 0.7660$$
$$= 3.064 \text{ cm}^2$$
$$\therefore \text{ Area of ABCD} = 6.13 \text{ cm}^2$$

Area of a triangle; three sides known

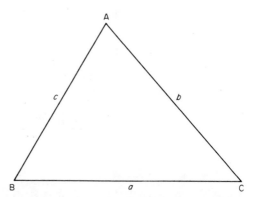

Fig. 6.8

In general, if the lengths of the three sides of a triangle are known, the solution of the triangle requires the application of the cosine rule. If only the area is required, the following rule is most useful since the calculation can be performed by a simple use of logarithm or square root tables.

$$\text{Perimeter} = 2s = a + b + c$$
$$\therefore \text{ Area} = \sqrt{\{s(s - a)(s - b)(s - c)\}}$$

Example 6.9. Calculate the area of a triangle whose sides have lengths of 3 cm, 5 cm, and 6 cm.

$$\text{Perimeter} = 2s = 14 \text{ cm}$$
$$\therefore s = 7$$
$$\therefore (s - a) = 7 - 3 = 4$$
$$\therefore (s - b) = 7 - 5 = 2$$
$$\therefore (s - c) = 7 - 6 = 1$$
$$\therefore \text{Area} = \sqrt{(7 \times 4 \times 2 \times 1)} = \sqrt{56}$$
$$= 7{\cdot}48 \text{ cm}^2$$

6.4. Application of sine and cosine rules to resultants of vectors

Example 6.10. In the given figure **AB** and **BC** are vectors representing the alternating currents in two branches of a parallel circuit. The line **AC** is the resultant or total current. If **AB** is equivalent to 20 A, **BC** is equivalent to 15 A, and ∠BCA is 30°, calculate the resultant current and the angle it makes with respect to **AB**.   U.L.C.I.

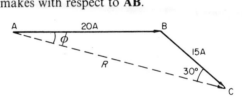

Fig. 6.9

Let **AC** represent R amp at an angle of ϕ with **AB**. By use of the sine rule,

$$\frac{\sin \phi}{15} = \frac{\sin 30°}{20}$$

$$\therefore \sin \phi = \frac{15 \sin 30°}{20}$$

$$= \frac{15 \times 0{\cdot}5}{20} = \frac{7{\cdot}5}{20} = 0{\cdot}375$$

$$\therefore \phi = 22° \, 2' \text{ or } 157° \, 58'$$

Since ∠BCA is 30°, ϕ cannot equal 157° 58', the total of these two angles then exceeding 180°.

$$\therefore \angle ABC = 180° - (22° \, 2' + 30°) = 127° \, 58'$$

By use of the sine rule,

$$\frac{R}{\sin 127° \; 58'} = \frac{20}{\sin 30°}$$

$$\therefore R = \frac{20 \times \sin 127° \; 58'}{\sin 30°}$$

$$= \frac{20 \times \sin 52° \; 2'}{\sin 30°}$$

$$= \frac{20 \times 0·7884}{0·5}$$

$$= 31·5 \text{ A}$$

Example 6.11. A mass of 98 g is suspended by two strings the ends of which are fixed at the same horizontal level. The resulting triangle of forces is shown in the given figure. AB represents the force exerted by the 98 g mass, BC the tension T_1 in one string and CA the tension T_2 in the other. The angle B is 52° and the angle A is 48°. Calculate the tensions T_1 and T_2.

C.G.L.I. T.T. (part Qn.)

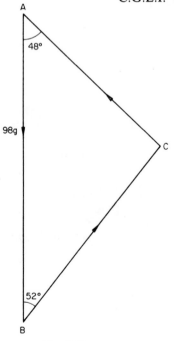

Fig. 6.10

It should be noted that Fig. 6.10 is a diagram of the three forces acting and not a diagram of the actual mass and strings. The length of AB, to some convenient scale, represents the force exerted vertically downwards by the 98 g mass. The calculation of the lengths BC and CA will then give the tensions T_1 and T_2.

By use of the sine rule,

$$\frac{AC}{\sin 52°} = \frac{98}{\sin 80°}$$

$$\therefore AC = \frac{98 \times \sin 52°}{\sin 80°}$$

$$= 78\cdot4 \text{ g} \quad \text{(S.R.)}$$

Similarly

$$\frac{BC}{\sin 48°} = \frac{98}{\sin 80°}$$

$$\therefore BC = \frac{98 \times \sin 48°}{\sin 80°}$$

$$= 74 \text{ g} \quad \text{(S.R.)}$$

The tensions in the strings, exerted by these equivalent masses in grammes is converted into newtons.

$$(454 \text{ g} = 1 \text{ lb}; \text{ and } 1 \text{ lbf} = 4\cdot448 \text{ N})$$

$$\therefore T_1 = 0\cdot725 \text{ N and } T_2 = 0\cdot767 \text{ N}$$

Example 6.12. In triangle ABC, AB = 11 cm, AC = 7 cm, and $\cos A = \frac{13}{77}$. Show that the side BC = 12 cm and $\sin A = (24\sqrt{10})/77$. Calculate the area of the triangle and deduce the values of sin B and sin C in the same form as sin A.

C.G.L.I. T.T.

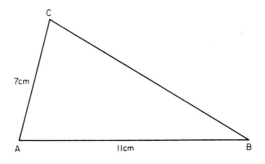

Fig. 6.11

Given two sides and the included angle, we use the cosine rule.

$$\therefore BC^2 = 7^2 + 11^2 - 2 \times 7 \times 11 \times \cos A$$

$$= 49 + 121 - 2 \times 77 \times \frac{13}{77}$$

$$= 170 - 26$$

$$= 144$$

$$\therefore BC = 12 \text{ cm}$$

$$\text{Area of } \triangle ABC = \sqrt{\{s(s-a)(s-b)(s-c)\}}$$

$$\text{where} \quad 2s = 7 + 11 + 12$$

$$\therefore s = 15$$

$$\therefore \text{area} = \sqrt{(15 \times 8 \times 4 \times 3)}$$

$$= \sqrt{(4 \times 360)}$$

$$= 2 \times 6 \times \sqrt{10}$$

$$= 12\sqrt{10} \text{ cm}^2$$

$$\therefore \tfrac{1}{2}bc \sin A = \text{area} = 12\sqrt{10}$$

$$\therefore \tfrac{1}{2} \times 7 \times 11 \sin A = 12\sqrt{10}$$

$$\therefore \sin A = \frac{1}{77}(24\sqrt{10})$$

Similarly
$$\tfrac{1}{2}ab \sin C = 12\sqrt{10}$$

$$\therefore \tfrac{1}{2} \times 12 \times 7 \times \sin C = 12\sqrt{10}$$

$$\therefore \sin C = \frac{1}{84}(24\sqrt{10})$$

and
$$\tfrac{1}{2}ac \sin B = 12\sqrt{10}$$

$$\therefore \tfrac{1}{2} \times 12 \times 11 \times \sin B = 12\sqrt{10}$$

$$\therefore \sin B = \frac{1}{132}(24\sqrt{10})$$

EXERCISE 6.1

1. (a) Find from mathematical tables the values of

   (i) sec 162°,   (ii) cot (−25°),   (iii) cosec 220°.

   (b) The given figure shows the girders supporting the roof of a
   workshop where AB = 19·2 m. By applying the sine rule to
   triangle ABD, show that the length of BD is 12·1 m. Hence
   calculate the length of DC and AC.

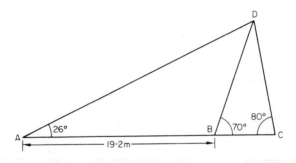

Fig. 6.12

C.G.L.I. T.T.

2. With the usual notation for a triangle ABC with angles A, B, and
   C, sides a, b, and c and the area $\triangle$, establish the formulae,

   (a) $\dfrac{a}{\sin A} = \dfrac{b}{\sin B} = \dfrac{c}{\sin C}$

   (b) $\triangle = \frac{1}{2}bc \sin A$

   (c) $2\triangle \sin A = a^2 \sin B \sin C$

   Calculate the area of a triangle having A = 52°, B = 49°, and
   a = 7·6 cm.

C.G.L.I. T.T.

3. (a) Evaluate using tables, (i) sin 560°, (ii) cos (5π/6),
   (iii) tan (−160°).
   (b) In the given figure, XB represents a vertical tower 40 m high.
   From a point A, the angle of elevation of X is 35°. A, B, and C are
   all at the same horizontal level such that ∠ BAC = 43°, ∠ BCA =
   52°. Show that BC = 49·45 m and calculate the angle of elevation
   of X from C.

Fig. 6.13

C.G.L.I. T.T.

4. The cosine rule states that,

$$a^2 = b^2 + c^2 - 2bc \cos A$$

Transpose the formula to give cos A in terms of the other quantities and hence find in degrees and minutes the value of the smallest angle in a triangle whose sides are 4, 5, and 6 m respectively.

E.M.E.U. (part Qn.)

5. An overhead conductor carrying electrical power, runs straight from A to B, a distance of 4 km. C is the position of a factory some distance from the line AB, and $\angle CAB = 46° 45'$ and $\angle CBA = 62° 17'$. It is desired to transmit power to the factory by erecting the shortest length of line from C to the conductor. Find the length of this line and the distance from A at which it will meet the main conductor.

E.M.E.U.

6. In a triangle ABC, side AB is 10 cm long, angle ABC is 135°, and angle ACB is 15°. Calculate the length of the side BC.

U.L.C.I. (part Qn.)

7. In a triangle ABC the side AB is 10 cm long, angle CAB is 30°, and angle ACB is 45°. Draw the triangle and calculate

   (a) the length of the side BC,
   (b) the angle ABC,
   (c) the length of side AC,
   (d) the area of the triangle.   U.L.C.I. (part Qn.)

8. Determine the vectorial sum of i_1 and i_2 by use of the cosine and sine rules if $i_1 = 20 \sin \theta$ and $i_2 = 30 \sin (\theta + \pi/3)$.

9. In a triangle ABC the side AB is 8 cm long. The angles ABC and BAC are 100° and 30° respectively. Calculate the length of the side BC.
                                                      U.L.C.I. (part Qn.)

10. Two hooks P, Q are fixed 1·05 m apart in a horizontal beam, and cords OP, OQ support a weight at O. If OP = 0·65 m, OQ = 0·8 m, calculate angle OPQ, and hence the depth of O below the beam.
                                                      C.G.L.I. T.T. (part Qn.)

11. (a) State the formulae which would be employed in solving a triangle (i) when given three sides, (ii) when given two sides and one angle which is not included between the sides.
    (b) The vector diagram of a certain electrical network is shown in the given figure. If AB = 5, BC = 14, and angle CAB = 22°, calculate the magnitude of the resultant vector AC.

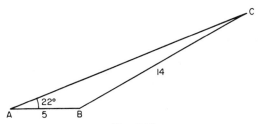

Fig. 6.14

12. Find the shortest side of a triangle whose perimeter is 30 m, given that the angles are 30°, 50°, and 100°.

13. Two radar stations A and B are 50 km apart, B being due East of A. The bearing of an aircraft is reported simultaneously from A as N 50° E and from B as N 30° W. Calculate its distance from B.

14. The figure shows the profile of a metal component in which the arcs whose centres are P and Q have radii 15 mm. Calculate the distances AP and AQ.

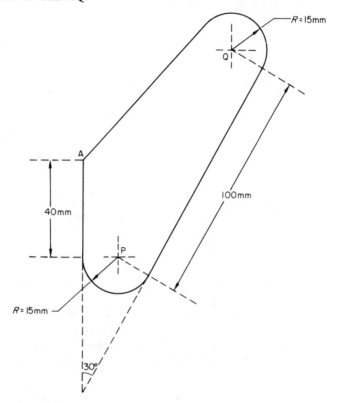

Fig. 6.15

6.5 Trigonometrical identities

If $x^2 - 3x = 0$, it is possible to find only two values of x which satisfy this relation; these values are said to be the solutions of the equation.

If $x^2 - 3x = x(x - 3)$, then the relation is true for all values of x, the r.h.s. being simply an alternative method of expressing the l.h.s. In this case the relation is called an 'identity' and not an equation.

From Pythagoras' theorem, in Fig. 6.16,

$$a^2 + c^2 = b^2$$

$$\therefore \frac{a^2}{b^2} + \frac{c^2}{b^2} = 1$$

$$\therefore \sin^2 \theta + \cos^2 \theta = 1 \qquad (6.1)$$

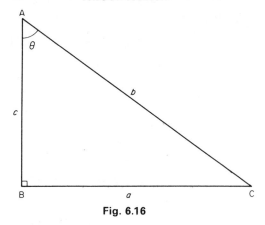

Fig. 6.16

Since this is true for all values of θ, the relation (6.1) is a trigonometrical identity. From the same figure,

$$\sin \theta = a/b \quad \text{and} \quad \cos \theta = c/b$$

$$\therefore \frac{\sin \theta}{\cos \theta} = \frac{a}{b} \div \frac{c}{b} = \frac{a}{b} \times \frac{b^1}{c} = \frac{a}{c}$$

$$\therefore \frac{\sin \theta}{\cos \theta} = \tan \theta \tag{6.2}$$

From (6.1), dividing by $\cos^2 \theta$,

$$\frac{\sin^2 \theta}{\cos^2 \theta} + 1 = \frac{1}{\cos^2 \theta}$$

$$\therefore \tan^2 + 1 = \sec^2 \theta \tag{6.3}$$

From (6.1), dividing by $\sin^2 \theta$,

$$1 + \frac{\cos^2 \theta}{\sin^2 \theta} = \frac{1}{\sin^2 \theta}$$

$$\therefore 1 + \cot^2 \theta = \operatorname{cosec}^2 \theta \tag{6.4}$$

There are many trigonometrical identities, of which (6.1) to (6.4) are the simplest; the student will find it useful to commit these to memory.

Example 6.13. Prove that

$$(\cos\theta - \sin\theta)(\cos\theta + \sin\theta) = 1 - 2\cos^2\theta\tan^2\theta$$

$$\begin{aligned}
\text{r.h.s.} &= 1 - 2\cos^2\theta\tan^2\theta \\
&= 1 - 2\cos^2\theta\frac{\sin^2\theta}{\cos^2\theta} \\
&= 1 - 2\sin^2\theta \\
&= \sin^2\theta + \cos^2\theta - 2\sin^2\theta \\
&= \cos^2\theta - \sin^2\theta \\
&= (\cos\theta - \sin\theta)(\cos\theta + \sin\theta) \\
&= \text{l.h.s.}
\end{aligned}$$

$$\therefore\ (\cos\theta - \sin\theta)(\cos\theta + \sin\theta) = 1 - 2\cos^2\theta\tan^2\theta$$

Example 6.14. Prove that

$$\frac{2\tan\theta}{1 - \cos\theta} = \frac{2\sin\theta}{\sin^2\theta + \cos\theta - 1}$$

$$\begin{aligned}
\text{r.h.s.} &= \frac{2\sin\theta}{\sin^2\theta + \cos\theta - 1} \\
&= \frac{2\sin\theta}{1 - \cos^2\theta + \cos\theta - 1} \\
&= \frac{2\sin\theta}{\cos\theta - \cos^2\theta} \\
&= \frac{2\sin\theta}{\cos\theta(1 - \cos\theta)} \\
&= \frac{2\sin\theta}{\cos\theta} \times \frac{1}{1 - \cos\theta} \\
&= \frac{2\tan\theta}{1 - \cos\theta}
\end{aligned}$$

$$\therefore\ \frac{2\tan\theta}{1 - \cos\theta} = \frac{2\sin\theta}{\sin^2\theta + \cos\theta - 1}$$

6.6 Trigonometrical equations

In solving trigonometrical equations, it is useful to recall the basic types of algebraic equations, particularly the quadratic equation and the use of factors.

Example 6.15.   Solve $\sin A - 2 \sin^2 A = 0$ for values of A from $0°$ to $360°$.

$$\sin A - 2 \sin^2 A = 0$$
$$\therefore \sin A(1 - 2 \sin A) = 0$$

Either

$$\sin A = 0$$
$$\therefore A = 0° \text{ or } 180°$$

or

$$1 - 2 \sin A = 0$$
$$\therefore 2 \sin A = 1$$
$$\therefore \sin A = \tfrac{1}{2}$$
$$\therefore A = 30° \text{ or } 150°$$

The solutions are therefore $0°$, $30°$, $150°$, or $180°$.

Example 6.16.   Solve $4 \sin B = -0·58$ for values of B from $0°$ to $360°$.

$$4 \sin B = -0·58$$
$$\therefore \sin B = \frac{-0·58}{4} = -0·145$$

We read the value $0·145$ in sine tables, giving an angle of $8° \ 20'$, but since $\sin B$ is negative, the solutions must lie in quadrants 3 ($180–270°$) and 4 ($270–360°$)

Hence

$$B = 180° + 8° \ 20' \text{ or } 360° - 8° \ 20'$$
$$\therefore B = 188° \ 20' \text{ or } 351° \ 40'$$

Example 6.17.   Solve $8 - 6 \sin^2 \theta - 7 \cos \theta = 0$.
In this equation, the unknown quantity, θ, is in two forms, $\sin^2 \theta$ and $\cos \theta$. Before solving, we must reduce these two unknowns to one; this is an instance when the trigonometrical identities are particularly useful.

$$8 - 6 \sin^2 \theta - 7 \cos \theta = 0$$
$$\therefore 8 - 6(1 - \cos^2 \theta) - 7 \cos \theta = 0$$
$$\therefore 8 - 6 + 6 \cos^2 \theta - 7 \cos \theta = 0$$
$$\therefore 6 \cos^2 \theta - 7 \cos \theta + 2 = 0$$
$$\therefore (3 \cos \theta - 2)(2 \cos \theta - 1) = 0$$

Either
$$3 \cos \theta - 2 = 0$$
$$\therefore \cos \theta = \tfrac{2}{3} = 0 \cdot 6667$$

or
$$2 \cos \theta - 1 = 0$$
$$\therefore \cos \theta = \tfrac{1}{2}$$

From cosine tables, we read the value 0·6667, giving $\theta = 48° \, 11'$, but $\cos \theta$ is also positive in quadrant 4 (270–360°). Hence,

$$\theta = 48° \, 11' \text{ or } 360°-48° \, 11'$$
$$= 48° \, 11' \text{ or } 311° \, 49'$$

Similarly, from $\cos \theta = \tfrac{1}{2}$,

$$\theta = 60° \text{ or } 300°$$

Example 6.18.   Solve $3 \sin A - 4 \cos A = 0$.

$$3 \sin A - 4 \cos A = 0$$
$$\therefore 3 \sin A = 4 \cos A$$
$$\therefore \frac{3 \sin A}{\cos A} = \frac{4 \cos A}{\cos A}$$
$$\therefore 3 \tan A = 4$$
$$\therefore \tan A = \frac{4}{3} = 1 \cdot 3333$$

From tangent tables, we read the value 1·3333, giving $A = 53° \, 8'$. Since $\tan A$ is positive, the angle A is in quadrants 1 (0–90°) or 3 (180–270°). Hence,

$$A = 53° \, 8' \text{ or } 180° + 53° \, 8'$$
$$= 53° \, 8' \text{ or } 233° \, 8'$$

Example 6.19.   If $\sin B = \tfrac{3}{5}$, write down without the use of tables the values of (a) $\cos B$, (b) $\cos (90° + B)$, (c) $\tan (180° - B)$.

Illustrate the given information by a diagram.

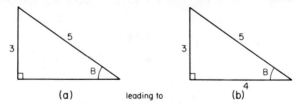

(a)   leading to   (b)

Fig. 6.17

6. $x\{x[x(3\cdot29) + 2\cdot18] - 4\cdot23\} + 5\cdot67 = 91\cdot0654$

Answer: 91·07

(Time: 43 sec)

Conclusions

(a) There is a wide range of automatic, electric, and electronic calculators which are naturally more expensive than the manual models but they do not have the basic educational qualities of the latter.

(b) The majority of students, who are not 'aware' of mathematics, develop greater interest when calculators are used.

(c) If students learn to use manual calculators, they can readily change to more automatic machines.

Specimen Examination papers

Union of Lancashire and Cheshire Institutes Electrical Technicians' Course (Second Year) Mathematics 1967

1. (a) Evaluate (i) $625^{-1/4}$, (ii) $a^{1/2} \times a^{-5/2} \times a^0$, given that $a = 4$.
   (b) If $Z = \sqrt{\{R^2 + (2\pi f L)^2\}}$ calculate the value of Z if $R = 50,000$, $f = 6 \times 10^6/\pi$, and $L = 0.01$.

2. The e.m.f. E of a d.c. machine is directly proportional to the speed of rotation, N, the magnetic flux, ϕ, and the number of armature conductors Z. If $E = 500$ when $N = 1000$, $\phi = 0.1$ and $Z = 300$, calculate the constant of proportionality. If N were reduced to 800, to what value must ϕ be adjusted to maintain the value of E at 500, Z being constant at 300?

3. A crate contains steel ball-bearings each of $\frac{1}{2}$ cm diameter. The total weight of the crate and its contents is 1600 g. If the crate weighs 69 g and 1 cubic cm of steel weighs 7.8 g, calculate the number of steel balls in the crate.

4. Solve the equations:

   (a) $2 \log x = 2.3522$
   (b) $\tan^2 \theta = 1$ (for values of θ from $0°$ to $360°$)

   (c) $\dfrac{4x}{5} + \dfrac{3y}{2} = 23$

   $\dfrac{7x}{4} - \dfrac{15y}{4} = 36.25$

5. (a) Factorize $4x^2 - 4x - 8$
   (b) What are the values of x which make the expression

$$(2x + 1)(x - 2)$$

   equal to zero?

   (c) Solve the equation $\dfrac{x + 1}{x - 1} = x - 2.$

6. The following figures are thought to obey a law of the form $y = mx + c$. Plot a graph and use it to find the values of m and c. What is the value of x when y is zero?

x	1·0	1·5	2·0	2·5	3·0	3·5
y	8	7	6	5	4	3

7. Plot the graph of $y = 2x^2 - 6$ between the values of $x = 3$ and $x = -3$.
   What are the values of x and y at the lowest point on the graph? What name is given to a curve of this type?

8. A chord is drawn through an 8 cm diameter circle and divides the radius to which it is perpendicular in the ratio 3:1. Show, by means of two separate diagrams, that two chords can be drawn which do this. Calculate the length of the shorter chord and the angle it subtends at the centre of the circle (a) in degrees, (b) in radians.

9. (a) Sketch the curves of the trigonometrical functions $\sin \theta$, $\cos \theta$, and $\tan \theta$, showing how each function varies as θ varies from $0°$ to $360°$.
   (b) Calculate the area of a triangle ABC given that angle ACB = $120°$, BC = 12 cm, and angles BAC and ABC are equal.

City and Guilds of London Institute Telecommunication Technicians' Course Mathematics A, 1967

1. (a) Simplify:
   (i) $(a^{1/3} - a^{-1/3})(a^{2/3} + 1 + a^{-2/3})$
   (ii) $(a^{1/3} + a^{-1/3})(a^{2/3} - 1 + a^{-2/3})$
   (iii) the result of dividing (i) by (ii).

(b) Factorize:

  (i) $6x^2 + x - 2$
  (ii) $2x^2 - 3x + 1$

and use your results to simplify,

$$\frac{1}{2x^2 - 3x + 1} - \frac{1}{6x^2 + x - 2}$$

giving your answer as one fraction.

2. Solve the equations:

  (a) $(0 \cdot 685)^{-(x+1)} = 0 \cdot 987$
  (b) $\log_{10}(x + 2) = 0 \cdot 578$
  (c) $\log 12 - \log 32 + 3 \log 2 = x \log 3$

3. (a) Solve for r and R the equations,

$$ar + bR = V$$
$$br - aR = v$$

  (b) $(x + 3)$, $(x + 8)$, $(x + 18)$ are the first three numbers of a sequence, such that the second divided by the first equals the third divided by the second. Calculate x and write down the fourth number of the sequence.

4. In Fig. E.1 ABC is a semi-circle centre O, with AB = 4 cm and BC = 3 cm. Show that,

  (i) the total area of the two segments is $3 \cdot 82$ cm^2
  (ii) the sine of angle BOC is $\frac{24}{25}$ and calculate the areas of the two sectors.

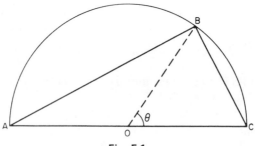

Fig. E.1

5. In Fig. E.2 the angle of elevation of the top X of a vertical aerial mast AX, height 40 m, from a point B due South is 42°. A point C

is located North 35° East of B at a distance of 80 m. If A, B, C are on the same horizontal level, show that AC = 50·5 m and calculate the value of the angle ACX.

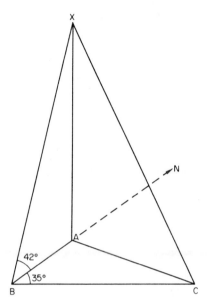

Fig. E.2

6. (a) With the usual convention for the sides and angles of a triangle ABC, show that, (i) $a = b \cos C + c \cos B$ and using the sine rule, (ii) $\sin A = \sin B \cos C + \sin C \cos B$ and verify formula (ii) when angle B = 25° and angle C = 115°.

(b) Find the value of θ between 0° and 360° which satisfies the equations,

$$\sin \theta = -0·8695 \quad \text{and} \quad \cos \theta = 0·4939$$

and find the value of $\tan \theta$.

7. Draw the graphs of $y_1 = 8x^2 + 22x - 21$ between $x = -4$ and $x = 2$ and $y_2 = 24/x$ between $x = -4$ and $x = -\frac{1}{2}$ and between $x = \frac{1}{2}$ and $x = 2$.

State the values of x when $y_1 = y_2$.

Between which values of x is $y_2 > y_1$?

8. (a) Express $x^2 + 6x - 4$ in the form $(x + a)^2 + b$ where a and b are constants. Hence solve the equation $x^2 + 6x - 4 = 0$.

   (b) Solve the equations,

   (i) $(50x - 31)^2 = 121$

   (ii) $\dfrac{3}{3x - 1} - \dfrac{2}{3x + 2} = 1$

9. In Fig. E.3 a cathode-ray tube has an outer casing consisting of an open cylinder, length 60 mm and diameter 45 mm, connected to part of a cone having a base diameter 180 mm. The distance between the base and the end of the cylinder is 90 mm. Show that the height of the complete cone of which part is shown is equal to 120 mm and calculate the total outside surface area of the tube.

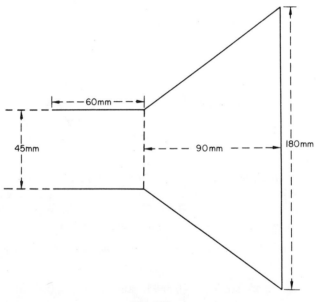

Fig. E.3

10. Solve graphically for values of θ between $0°$ and $180°$, the equations,

   (a) $\cos \theta = \sin 2\theta$

   (b) $\tan \theta = \sin 2\theta$

Answers to Exercises

EXERCISE 1.1

1. 10·46
2. 0·9772
3. 0·09703
4. 0·04211
5. 0·009018
6. 56·44
7. 0·2874
8. 121·8
9. 6·616
10. 20,290
11. 895·4
12. 9·988
13. 0·9865
14. 2·106
15. 0·002123
16. 0·168
17. 7·534
18. 0·076
19. (a) 0·5; (b) 3·83
20. (a) 5×10^5; (b) 0·3641
21. 9·488
22. 50 mW

EXERCISE 1.2

1. 3
2. 3
3. 4
4. -2
5. $\frac{3}{2}$
6. $\frac{6}{5}$
7. -2
8. $\frac{1}{4}$
9. -4
10. 3
11. $\log_4 8$
12. $\log_7 10$
13. $\log_2 3$
14. $\log_b c$
15. $\log_e 10$
16. 0·4772
17. $2y + x; 2x - y; x - 2y$
18. 0·6990
19. $pv^n = 100$
20. (a) 0·77815; (b) 1·07918; (c) 1·43136; (d) 0·69897
21. $\log (P^{1/2}Q^2/10)$
22. $\frac{3}{2}$
23. (a) 2; (b) 3
24. 0·7692
25. $P = 100LD^2/\sqrt{W}$
26. $a = 80$
27. $x = -2$
28. $x = -2·119$
29. $V = 195$ V
30. 274 mA
31. $C = 101$; $V = 0·824$
32. $T_2 = 46·2$ N

EXERCISE 1.3

1. (a) 72; (b) 122 cm²
2. (a) $\frac{5}{32}$; (b) $\frac{1}{4}$
3. 3·96 cm
4. 0·465 cm
5. 76·9 cm³
6. 163·4 cm³
7. 5100 cm³
8. $h = 8r$
9. 3·65 cm

10. (a) 23·8 mm; (b) 17·8 mm; (c) 2·68 kg
11. 817 kg; 39·3 mm　　　　　　　**12.** 2·87%
13. (b) (i) 12 cm; (ii) 240°; (iii) 302 cm^2; (iv) 600 cm^3
14. 2 cm　　　　　　　　　　　　**15.** 462 g
16. (a) 148·9 cm; (b) 2·26 m^2　　**17.** 193 cm^2; 2·41 cm^3
18. (a) 318 cm^3; (b) 126 cm^2　　**19.** 0·812 m^3; 324·8 kg
20. 245 g

EXERCISE 2.1

1. AB and BC, 0·095 A; AD and DC, 0·068 A; CE, 0·163 A
2. AB, 0·42 A; CD, 0·27 A; FE, 0·15 A
3. AB and BC, 0·17 A; AC, 0·87 A; CD, 1·0 A
4. AB and DE, 0·11 A; CB, 0·62 A; BD, 0·73 A
5. AB and EF, 0·38 A; CD, 0·13 A; BE, 0·25 A
6. AB, 0·99 A; BC, 0·8 A; DE, 0·48 A; EF, 0·67 A; BE, 0·19 A
7. AB, 0·64 A; BC, 0·67 A; AD, 1·03 A; DC, 1·0 A; DB, 0·033 A
8. 9 Ω, 0·4 A; 4 Ω, 0·3 A; 12 Ω, 0·1 A; 6 Ω, 0·8 A
9. (a) $I_1 = 4$ A
　　(b) X − Y = +6 V; X − Z = +4 V; Z − Y = +2 V; $I_2 = 4$ A; $I_3 = 6$ A;
　　　 $R = 0·4 Ω$
10. (a) AB = 60 A; CD = 120 A; BD = 40 A; EF = 210 A; FG = 220 A;
　　　 GH = 170 A
　　(b) 8·2 W
11. (a) 3 A; (b) 12 V, 3 V; (c) 6 A
12. (a), (b) C − D, 3·2 A; B − E, 2·5 A; F − A, 5·7 A
13. $x = 90 Ω$; 0·05 A
14. From 0·67 A to 2 A. A break in the 12 Ω resistor.
15. 11 V, 12·5 V
16. $I_1 = 2·2, I_2 = 0·3$
17. $V_1 = 1·7, V_2 = 2·3$
18. $I_1 = 2·3, I_2 = 4·5$
19. $I_1 = −0·2, I_2 = 2·26$
20. $x = 3·6, y = −5·2$

EXERCISE 2.2

1. $3b(a^2 − 5b)$　　　　　　　　**2.** $(2x + 5y)(2x − 5y)$
3. $(2a + 3d)(b + 2c)$　　　　　**4.** $(5x + 1)(y − 3z)$
5. $(a − c)(a + b)$　　　　　　　**6.** $(1 − 3c)(1 + 3c)$
7. $2(p + 7q)(p − 7q)$　　　　　**8.** sin A (3 cos A − sin A)
9. tan B (2 tan B + 1)　　　　　**10.** $(1 − t)(1 + t − a)$
11. $(2b + 9c + 7d)(2b − 5c − 7d)$　**12.** $a(a − 1)(a + 1)$
13. $(x + 3)(x + 1)$　　　　　　　**14.** $(a − 4)(a − 2)$
15. $(b − 6)(b + 4)$　　　　　　　**16.** $(y + 8)(y − 5)$
17. $(c + 6)(c − 1)$　　　　　　　**18.** $(c − 3)(c − 2)$
19. $(3x + 4)(2x − 1)$　　　　　　**20.** $(5 + 4x)(2 − 3x)$

21. $(3x + 4)(2x + 3)$
22. $(9 + 5x)(2 + 3x)$
23. $(a + 10b)(a + 2b)$
24. $(5c + 7d)(4c - 5d)$
25. $(6b + 7)(5b - 6)$
26. $6, 2$
27. $-9, -5$
28. $\frac{1}{2}, -\frac{1}{3}$
29. $\frac{2}{5}, -\frac{3}{2}$
30. $-1, -\frac{8}{7}$
31. $\frac{2}{3}, -\frac{5}{6}$
32. $\frac{5}{8}, -\frac{3}{2}$
33. $\frac{5}{2}, \frac{5}{2}$
34. $0, 7$
35. $\frac{5}{2}, -1$

EXERCISE 2.3

1. $0{\cdot}520, 13{\cdot}5$
2. $0{\cdot}373, -5{\cdot}37$
3. $6{\cdot}67, -0{\cdot}675$
4. $-1, -\frac{8}{3}$
5. $0{\cdot}275, -7{\cdot}28$
6. $-0{\cdot}641, -9{\cdot}36$
7. $\dfrac{-q \pm \sqrt{(q^2 - pr)}}{p}$
8. $\dfrac{-n \pm \sqrt{(n^2 + 4ms)}}{2m}$
9. $-0{\cdot}697, -4{\cdot}30$
10. $0{\cdot}349, 2{\cdot}15$
11. $1{\cdot}14, -1{\cdot}47$
12. $1{\cdot}31, -0{\cdot}914$
13. $1{\cdot}98, -0{\cdot}303$
14. $0{\cdot}421, -4{\cdot}08$
15. $\dfrac{-b \pm \sqrt{(b^2 + 8ac)}}{4a}$
16. $\dfrac{-b \pm \sqrt{(b^2 - ac)}}{a}$

EXERCISE 2.4

1. $6{\cdot}14$ cm $\times$ $8{\cdot}14$ cm; $8{\cdot}86$ g/ml
2. $30°C$
3. $4{\cdot}13$ cm
4. 18 m
5. $2{\cdot}21$ sec
6. 9 cm $\times$ 12 cm
7. $0{\cdot}40$ cm
8. $7{\cdot}1$ cm
9. $5{\cdot}96$ cm^3, $20{\cdot}96$ cm^3
10. $12{\cdot}4$ m or $39{\cdot}2$ m
11. $4{\cdot}14$ cm
12. $5{\cdot}2$ cm
13. $6{\cdot}04$ m
14. $1{\cdot}42$ cm
15. $-9{\cdot}1$ V; $-2{\cdot}78$ V

EXERCISE 2.5

1. (a) $0, 4$; (b) $0{\cdot}55, 3{\cdot}4$
2. (a) $0, 5$; (b) $0{\cdot}85, 4{\cdot}2$
3. (a) $1, -4$; (b) $0{\cdot}56, -3{\cdot}6$
4. (a) 45 m; (b) 63 m; (c) 45 m
5. $-4{\cdot}3$; (a) $-0{\cdot}55, 3{\cdot}6$; (b) $-1, 4$
6. $(4{\cdot}7, 2{\cdot}7)$; $(1{\cdot}3, -0{\cdot}7)$
7. (a) $(2, 0)$; $(-1, -3)$; (b) $\pm2, +2$
8. $-6\frac{1}{4}; 2, -3$
9. (b) (i) $0{\cdot}65, 4{\cdot}85$; (ii) $0{\cdot}65$ to $4{\cdot}85$; (c) $4x^3 - 17x^2 - 15x + 15 = 0$
10. $2r + r\theta = 12$; 9 m^2; $r = 3$ m, $\theta = 2$ rad
11. $A = 2\pi r(r + 9\pi - 2\pi r)$; $r = 3{\cdot}3$ cm; $h = 7{\cdot}5$ cm
12. (a) 2500 m; (b) $12{\cdot}5$ sec; (c) $3{\cdot}5$ sec, $21{\cdot}5$ sec
13. $2{\cdot}6$
14. 9 m
15. (a) 14 cm; (b) 50 cm^2; (c) $10{\cdot}8$ cm; $16{\cdot}8$ cm

EXERCISE 3.1

1. $W = 4·85d^2$; 6·19 kg; 3·06 mm **2.** 144

3. 3·5 **4.** $a = 86, b = -994$

5. (a) $R = Kl/d^2$; (b) $K = 5·63 \times 10^{-6}$; (c) $l = 178$ cm

6. (a) 4% decrease; (b) (i) 40 m, (ii) 2·4 MHz

7. (a) $E = (0·86 \, H\sqrt{P})/D^2$; (b) $E = 15·4$ μA/m

8. Reduced 12:1 **9.** $k = 2 \times 10^{-4}$; $R = 18·2$ kΩ

10. (a) Reduced 4; 3; (b) $100(2xy + y^2)/x^2$

11. (b) $E = 638/d^2$ **12.** 3·51 kJ

13. 4:1 **14.** $W = k\rho d^3$; 20 g

15. $k = 16 \times 10^{-4}$; $S = 2 \times 10^{-4}$ **16.** $k = \frac{1}{10}$

17. 0·5% decrease **18.** 16:25

19. 9·5% increase **20.** 4·7% increase

EXERCISE 3.2

1. $y \to x^2$ Gradient a, intercept b

2. $y \to x$,, m,   ,, c

3. $E \to 1/I$,, k ,, c

4. $s/t \to t$,, $\frac{1}{2}f$,, u

5. $z^2 \to X^2$,,   1   ,, K

6. $y/x \to 1/x^2$,, a ,, b

  or $yx \to x^2$,, b ,, a

7. $1/y \to x$,, $1/a$,, b/a

8. $1/y \to x$,, a ,, b

9. $1/y \to x^2$,, $1/a$,, b/a

10. $y\sqrt{x} \to x$,, a ,, b

11. $a = 10, b = 4$ **12.** $n = 2, a = 10, b = 4$

13. $a = -0·12, b = 0·032$ **14.** $k = 13·8, c = 5·6$

15. $a = 0·28, b = 0·017$ **16.** $a = 0·6, b = 6$

17. $P = aN + bN^2, a = 0·1, b = 2 \times 10^{-4}$

18. $a = 100$ **19.** $k = 20, c = 100$

20. $n = 3·8, a = 1·23 \times 10^{-6}$ **21.** $k = 72, a = 1·03$

22. $B = 1·54 \times 10^{-3}E^{2·6}$ **23.** $k = 2·51, n = 1·8$

24. $n = -1·2, a = 0·67$ **25.** $n = 1·38, C = 550$

EXERCISE 3.3

1. $e = \dfrac{Erx}{R(r + x) - x^2}$, $e = \frac{3}{4}$

2. $L = \dfrac{1}{4\pi^2f^2C}$, $L = 1·1 \times 10^{-4}$

3. $C = \dfrac{4L}{4\omega^2L^2 + R^2}$

4. $C = \dfrac{L}{4\pi^2L^2f_r^2 + R^2}$; $C = 7·5 \times 10^{-5}$

5. $L_1 = \dfrac{L_2}{4\pi^2 f^2 L_2 - 1}$; $L_2 = \dfrac{L_1}{4\pi^2 f^2 L_1 - 1}$

6. $X_2 = X_1 - \sqrt{(Z^2 - R^2)}$

7. (a) $Z = 23 \cdot 1\,\Omega$; (b) $f = \dfrac{1}{2\pi\sqrt{LC}}$

8. $R = 2\sqrt{\left(\dfrac{L - \omega^2 L^2 C}{C}\right)}$

9. $b = \dfrac{1}{h}\sqrt{(4k^2 + 3ah^2)}$; $b = \sqrt{6} = 2 \cdot 45$

10. $L = \dfrac{\sqrt{(V^2 - I^2 R^2)}}{\omega I} + \dfrac{1}{\omega^2 C}$

11. $R_1 = \dfrac{R_2(R - R_2)}{(2R_2 - R)}$

12. $\mu = \dfrac{G(R + r)}{R(1 - G)}$

EXERCISE 4.1

1. (a) 300 mm	(b) 241 mm	(c) 193 mm
2. (a) 170 mm	(b) 113 mm	(c) 91·8 mm
3. (a) 60 mm	(b) 80 mm	(c) 89·3 mm
4. (a) 20°	(b) 20°	(c) 70°
(d) 60°	(e) 60°	(f) 60°
(g) 30°	(h) 70°	(i) 30°
(j) 60°		

5. 69·3 mm   **6.** 292 mm   **7.** 50 mm

8. 41·4 mm   **9.** 105 mm   **10.** 48·8 cm^2

11. (a) 68 mm^2 (b) 36·1 mm   (c) 57·2 mm

12. 21·3 mm   **13.** 40 mm; 73° 44′

15. (a) 518 mm^2; (b) (i) 52·7 mm, (ii) 31° 47′, (iii) 42·5 mm

16. (a) 12·75 cm; (b) (i) 65°, (ii) 25°, (iii) 300 mm, (iv) 420 cm^2

17. 6, 25°   **18.** $2r + r\theta = 12$; 9 m^2; 3m; 114·6° (2 rad)

19. (a) (i) 66°, (ii) 91·4 mm, (iii) 6550 mm^2
    (b) (i) 66°, (ii) 182·8 mm, (iii) 262 cm^2

20. (a) 2 rad, (b) 114·6°

21. (a) $\dfrac{5\pi}{3}$ (= 5·24 rad); (b) (i) 524 mm, (ii) 262 cm^2

22. (a) 50 mm, 33° 42′   **23.** $\angle$ TAC = 25°; $\angle$ TBC = 115°

24. (a) 56 mm   (b) 420 mm^2 (c) 120° 30′

25. (a) 419 mm^2 (b) $1\frac{1}{3}$

26. (i) 42° 30′; (ii) 5·24 m/s   **27.** 35 cm^2

EXERCISE 5.1

1. (a) 0·9063	(b) −0·9659	(c) −0·7813
(d) −0·4226	(e) 1·1918	(f) −0·1736
(g) −0·8660	(h) 0·7660	(i) −0·3640
(j) 0·1736		

2. (a) 1·064   (b) 1·015   (c) 1·429
   (d) 1·743   (e) −1·035   (f) 0·5774
   (g) 1·743   (h) 2·924   (i) 1·732
   (j) −1·743

3. (a) 0·2588   (b) 3·564   (c) 2·5173
   (d) 0·4924   (e) 0·5977   (f) 0·5000
   (g) 1·495   (h) −0·8452   (i) 0·8391
   (j) 2·000

4. (a) −0·64   (b) 228°, 312°

5. (a) −0·26   (b) $4\pi/15$, $26\pi/15$

6. π rad, 3   **7.** $2\pi/3$ rad, 2

8. $14\pi/45$, $59\pi/45$ rad   **9.** $\pi/4$, $5\pi/4$ rad   **10.** $y = 4 \sin 2\theta$

EXERCISE 5.2

1. (a) 50·0 Hz   (b) 250 Hz   (c) 20·0 Hz
   (d) 318 Hz   (e) 10^5 Hz

2. (a) 79·5 Hz   (b) 35·0 Hz   (c) 71·6 Hz
   (d) 500 Hz   (e) 1590 Hz

3. (a) 1440 rad/s   (b) 9430 rad/s   (c) 2×10^4 rad/s
   (d) 2π rad/s   (e) 1 rad/s

4. (a) $\pi \times 10^3$ rad/s   (b) 2 rad/s   (c) $1·08 \times 10^2$ rad/s
   (d) 2000 rad/s   (e) $2\pi f$ rad/s

5. (a) (i) −0·7378, (ii) 0·9397   (b) $3\pi/4$ (c) −50

6. (a) 38·6   (b) 60 ; 0·0059

7. (a) 100 A, 1/40 sec   (b) −70·7 A
   (c) 0·00312, (= 1/320 sec)

8. (a) −0·7660   (b) 59·6 V

9. 0·250, 0·583 sec

10. (a) 1/300, 1/150 sec   (b) −10 A   (c) 10 A

11. (a) −4·99, −4·99   (b) $1·59 \times 10^{-4}$ sec

12. (a) 230 V, 1/50 sec, 50 Hz   (b) 0·00238 sec

13. (a) 200 A, 1/150 sec, 150 Hz   (b) 8 A

14. (a) 3·99 A, 3·99 A   (b) $i = 0$, $t = 0·00484$ sec ; $i = 40$, $t = 0·00234$ sec

15. (a) 14·1 A, −14·1 A   (b) 1/400 sec   (c) 1/1200 sec

16. (a) 10 A   (b) 50 V

17. 50 Hz, $i = 20 \sin \left(100\pi t + \dfrac{\pi}{6} \right)$

18. (a) 55·7 Hz   (b) 0·00122 sec

19. (a) 50 A, 100 V   (b) 90°, v leads i

20. 41·7 Hz, $-\dfrac{2\pi}{3}$; $v = V_m \sin (2\pi f t + \phi)$

EXERCISE 5.3

1. $I_{av} = 2·55$ A, $I = 2·83$ A

2. $\pi/6$ rad, $f = 50$ Hz, $i =$ zero

3. $V_{av} = 6·4$ V, $V = 7·1$ V

4. $I_{av} = 10$ A, $I = 11·5$ A

5. $I_{av} = 13·8$ A, $I = 15·7$ A (mid-ordinate), $I = 16·3$ A (Simpson)

6. $I_{av} = 7·5$ A, $I = 7·9$ A, form factor = 1·05

7. $V = 111$ V   **8.** $I_m = 70·7$ A   **9.** $V = 389$ V

EXERCISE 5.4

1. $5 \cdot 3 \sin (\omega t + 0 \cdot 33)$
2. $14 \cdot 6 \sin (\omega t - 0 \cdot 35)$
3. $58 \cdot 3 \sin (\theta - 0 \cdot 51)$
4. $57 \cdot 5 \sin (2\pi ft + 0 \cdot 66)$
5. $3 \cdot 66 \sin (2\pi ft - 0 \cdot 4)$
6. $16 \sin (\omega t - 1 \cdot 95)$
7. $13 \cdot 2 \sin (\theta - 1 \cdot 75)$
8. $10 \cdot 2 \sin (\theta - 2 \cdot 63)$
9. $25_{57°}$
10. $13 \cdot 3_{85°}$
11. $i = 13 \cdot 2 \sin (\theta + 0 \cdot 33)$
12. (a) 60° 30′; (b) 106°
13. $i_R = 130 \sin (100\pi t + 1 \cdot 17)$
15. 150 V, 30°
16. $V_R = 115 \sin (\theta + 7°)$
17. 31·6 A, 22°
18. (a) $R = 9 \cdot 1$ at 56·7° to i_1
     (b) $R = 9 \cdot 1$ at 57° to i_1
19. $0 \cdot 63_{-51 \cdot 2°}$, $0 \cdot 63_{128 \cdot 8}$
20. (a) (i) $-0 \cdot 7660$, (ii) 59·6 V; (b) 275 V

EXERCISE 6.1

1. (a) (i) $-1 \cdot 052$, (ii) $-2 \cdot 145$, (iii) $-1 \cdot 556$
    (b) DC = 11·54 m; AC = 25·34 m   **2.** 27·2 cm^2
3. (a) (i) $-0 \cdot 3420$, (ii) $-0 \cdot 8660$, (iii) $0 \cdot 3640$;   (b) 38° 58′
4. $\cos A = \dfrac{b^2 + c^2 - a^2}{2bc}$; 41° 24′
5. 2·73 km, 2·57 km   **6.** 19·3 cm
7. (a) 7·07 cm; (b) 105°; (c) 13·7 cm; (d) 34·2 cm^2
8. $43 \cdot 6 \sin (\theta + 0 \cdot 639)$ **9.** BC = 5·22 cm
10. 49° 35′: 0·495 m   **11.** (b) AC = 18·5
12. 6·66 m   **13.** 32·6 km
14. AP = 42·7 mm; AQ = 80·0 mm

EXERCISE 6.2

1. (a) 74 m   (b) 74 m   (c) 18°
2. (a) (i) 27° 28′, 152° 32′; (ii) 45° 15′, 314° 45′; (iii) 135°, 315°
    (c) (i) 533 m; (ii) 31° 24′ E of N
3. (a) $\dfrac{1}{\sqrt{(1 + x^2)}}$
4. (a) 120°, 131° 49′, 228° 11′, 240°   **5.** 30°, 150°, 221° 49′, 318° 11′
6. (c) 120°, 300°
7. (a) 15°, 75°, 195°, 255°   (b) $2/\sqrt{3}, \sqrt{3}$
8. (b) 0°, 112° 37′
9. (a) $\dfrac{\sqrt{(k^2 - 1)}}{k}, \dfrac{1}{\sqrt{(k^2 - 1)}}$
    (b) (i) 68·7 m   (ii) 84·5 m   (iii) 28° 12′
10. (a) (i) 0·2014   (ii) $-0 \cdot 3822$ (iii) -1
     (b) (i) 39·3 m   (ii) 70·2 m   (iii) 60° 48′
11. (a) (i) 37° 42′, 142° 18′   (ii) 64° 24′, 295° 36′
     (iii) 120°, 300°
     (b) 38° 10′   **12.** 56°
13. (a) $3\frac{3}{4}$ (b) $\bar{1} \cdot 9134$
14. (a) $\sqrt{(x^2 - 1)}/x, 1/(x^2 - 1)$ **15.** 4·43 cm

16. (a) 19·3 cm   (b) 60°, 120°, 240°, 300°
17. (a) $5·57 \times 10^{-5}$ (b) 5·22 cm
18. (a) 13°, 77°
     (b) (i) 1° 48′   (ii) 3° 49′   (iii) 42° 58′
19. (a) $\frac{1}{4}$ (b) (i) −0·9377   (ii) −0·7063
20. A = 47° 58′ or 132° 2′ ; B = 23° 54′ or 336° 6′
21. 45°, 161° 34′, 225°, 341° 34′   **22.** 58° 28′, 111° 34′
23. (a) (i) −0·6018   (ii) −1·1106   (iii) 0·7660
     (b) 247° 27′   (c) $2t/(1 - t^2)$
24. (a) (i) 0   (ii) −2·37
     (b) 4/5, $\frac{3}{4}$
     (c) cos A = $\frac{1}{2}$, sin B = $-\frac{1}{3}$
        A = 60°, 300° ; B = 199° 28′, 340° 32′

EXERCISE 7.1

1. 1·075	**2.** 15·3	**3.** 0·598
4. 0·737	**5.** 0·614	**6.** 0·390
7. 0·236	**8.** 17·5	**9.** 0·127
10. 1·405	**11.** 15·5	**12.** 1·16
13. 2·56	**14.** 1·85	**15.** 4·65, 31·8, 169
16. 29·4°	**17.** 47·3°	**18.** 43·4°
19. 24·2°	**20.** 71·1°	**21.** 85·7°
22. 0·0874	**23.** 1·72°	

24. $U = 180/\pi$; $L = \log_e 10$; $V = \pi/180$

EXERCISE 7.2

1. (a) 10010   (b) 100001   (c) 111100
     (d) 11100011   (e) 1111101000
2. (a) 3   (b) 21   (c) 56
     (d) 35   (e) 255
3. (a) 10111   (b) 110011   (c) 11011110
     (d) 110010   (e) 1001010
4. (a) 1010   (b) 110   (c) 101101
     (d) 10001   (e) 100010
5. (a) 100011   (b) 100001   (c) 10000010
     (d) 1101001   (e) 10001100101
6. (a) 101   (b) 1001   (c) 1101·00
     (d) 11·10   (e) 11·00

ANSWERS TO EXAMINATION PAPER
U.L.C.I. Electrical Technicians' Course
(Second Year) Mathematics 1967

1. (a) (i) 1/5, (ii) 1/16   (b) 13×10^4
2. 1/60, 0·125   **3.** 3000

4. (a) 15   (b) 45°, 135°, 225°, 315°
  (c) $x = 25, y = 2$
5. (a) $4(x - 2)(x + 1)$ (b) $-\frac{1}{2}, 2$ (c) 3·73, 0·27
6. $m = -2, c = 10; x = 5$ **7.** $x = 0, y = -6$; Parabola
8. 5·29 cm, 41° 24′, 0·7226   **9.** (b) $36\sqrt{3}$ ($=62·35$) cm^2

ANSWERS TO EXAMINATION PAPER

C.G.L.I. Telecommunication Technicians' Course, Mathematics A, 1967

1. (a) (i) $a - \dfrac{1}{a}$ (ii) $a + \dfrac{1}{a}$ (iii) $\dfrac{a^2 - 1}{a^2 + 1}$

  (b) (i) $(3x + 2)(2x - 1)$ (ii) $(2x - 1)(x - 1)$

$$\dfrac{2x + 3}{(2x - 1)(x - 1)(3x + 2)}$$

2. (a) $-1·035$ (b) 1·784   (c) 1
3. (a) $r = \dfrac{aV + bv}{a^2 + b^2}; R = \dfrac{bV - av}{a^2 + b^2}$ (b) 2; 40
4. 4·02; 5·80 cm^2 **5.** 38° 23′
6. (b) 299° 36′; $-1·7603$
7. $-3·25, -0·65, 1·25; -3·25$ to $-0·65; 0$ to $1·25$
8. (a) $(x + 3)^2 - 13; 0·61$ or $-6·61$ (b) (i) 0·84 or 0·4;   (ii) $\pm 1·054$
9. 737 cm^2
10. (a) 30°, 90°, 150°   (b) 0°, 45°, 135°, 180°

Index